"Spoo… by:

Trin… NW²

Trinity Mirror Nort… North Wales
PO Box …
Old Hall Street,
Liverpool L69 3EB

Business Development Director:
Mark Dickinson

Business Development Executive Editor:
Ken Rogers

Design / Production:
Colin Sumpter, Peter Grant

Words:
© Billy Roberts

ISBN 978 1 905266 87 6

CONTENTS

4: FOREWORD
6: INTRODUCTION

9: SINS OF THE FATHERS
12: A SOJOURN IN THE PAST
17: ENCOUNTERS IN THE CEMETERY
24: THE GHOSTLY GOINGS ON AT RIGBY'S PUB
28: APPARITION IN HOLY TRINITY
30: THE SOUTHPORT POLTERGEIST
35: THE MYSTERY OF THE PALACE HOTEL
37: EVIL GOINGS ON IN THE BASEMENT
39: THE GHOSTS OF CHURCHES
42: GHOSTS OF OLD HALL STREET
44: GHOSTS OF WORLD WAR TWO
47: THE CRYSTAL BALL
54: DOGGIE TAILS
59: HUMOROUS SIDE OF A SÉANCE
62: THE GHOST OF BLACKSTONE STREET
64: THE CURSED HOUSE
66: THE MYSTERY OF POLLY BRADSHAW
69: THE MYSTERY OF THE CAT WOMAN OF TOXTETH
72: GHOSTLY HOSPITAL TALES
77: DEAD MAN'S HANDWRITING
83: PARKLEA MANOR REVISITED
86: THE MYSTERY OF TERESA HELENA HIGGINSON
89: DEAD MAN'S MONEY
92: GHOSTS OF CENTRAL HALL
94: HAUNTED FURNITURE
103: CURSES FROM WORLD WAR TWO
108: THE FIRST WORLD WAR ANGEL OF THE TRENCHES

112: THE MYSTERY OF HEATHER
116: GHOSTLY PENNY LANE
119: THE GHOSTS OF GREENBANK PARK
122: THE GHOSTLY FUNERAL CORTEGE
127: SPOOKY DRAWINGS
130: THE HAUNTED VIOLIN
133: MYSTERIOUS GOINGS ON AT ST GEORGE'S HALL
141: GENIE IN THE BOTTLE AND A WISH THAT CAME TRUE
144: THE GHOSTS OF THURSTASTON
147: THE MYSTERY OF OLD MA' CLEGG
150: THE MYSTERY OF GEORGE GERMAIN FONEY
152: THE GHOSTS OF THE BLUECOAT
154: THE GHOSTS OF LEASOWE CASTLE
156: THE DEVIL IN BOOTLE
159: THE GHOSTS OF THE BALMORAL SUITE
161: SPRING HEELED JACK - FACT OR FICTION?
164: DESTINATION UNKNOWN
166: THE GHOSTS OF THE MYSTERY
169: THE MYSTERY OF KITTY WILKINSON
173: OLDFIELD FARM REVISITED
174: THE GHOSTLY LADY AND THE LITTLE GIRL
177: THE LITTLE BOY WHO SAW TRUE
180: THE UNINVITED LODGER
183: THINGS YOU WANTED TO KNOW
184: MISCELLANEOUS PIECES

190: MEDIA REVIEWS
191: WITH THANKS
192: ABOUT THE AUTHOR

FOREWORD

Everyone likes a ghost story and not just around halloween. Things that go bump in the night seem to appeal to people of all ages.

As a child I was brought up on the TV world of such programmes as the Twilight Zone, One Step Beyond and The Outer Limits. And movies too such as Dead of Night and The Sixth Sense.

I even loved the excitement of the ghost train at fairgrounds.

I have always loved twists in tales - the unexpected. The spookier the better.

In later life I was fascinated by the world of psychics - mediums and the other side (and I don't mean Birkenhead).

As a journalist for more than 30 years I remain sceptical but some things just cannot be explained.

I have seen what I believe to have been ghosts and experienced icy cold rooms and visited haunted houses always feeling something unusual had happened there.

I always read up on any article or book on the subject matter and that is why Spooky Liverpool - the first book in this series - was such an enjoyable read for me and thousands of other curious folk.

It's both scary and enthralling and packed with references to places in Liverpool that readers can relate to.

Indeed, ghost storytelling is an art form and there's no better exponent of the genre than Liverpool's celebrated psychic and author - Billy Roberts.

I have known him a long time and his enthusiasm and knowledge of the spirt world - whether on TV, radio, print and his website, is vast and varied.

Billy is a natural writer when it comes to making his stories gripping and concise and there are even flashes of gentle humour in lighter tales, but all focusing on the spirit world.

As with all his diverse work, Billy takes great pride in his research allowing the reader to make up his or her own mind.

Whether you are snuggled up in bed, in an airport lounge or relaxing on holiday Spooky 2 takes up where Spooky 1 left off.

It's another collection of compelling tales and ghostly goings-on from Liverpool - the capital of haunting.

And in this edition there's an extra bonus - some photographs from his own album that will make you look again and again, asking that spooky question 'is it or isn't it a ghost?'

Welcome to another world - Spooky Liverpool.

PETER GRANT
LIVERPOOL ECHO
JULY 2008

Front Cover picture was set up and taken by Jason Roberts,
Liverpool Daily Post and Echo photographer.

INTRODUCTION

Everybody is fascinated by ghost stories, or spooky tales and unexplainable mysteries. Even the sceptic has to admit to having some interest in the paranormal and things that go bump in the night. I can't really remember a time when I have not been interested in the paranormal and ghostly happenings. I have been psychic since I was a child, and as far back as I can remember seeing so-called 'dead' people has been commonplace to me. In fact, from as early as three I have been around some sort of paranormal phenomena, but it was only in my early thirties that I actually became a professional medium.

Whenever I have been invited to investigate paranormal phenomena, I have always looked for a rational explanation first of all. Although discarnate manifestations cannot be excluded from a typical 'haunted location,' I have learned that not all phenomena is the result of discarnate intervention, and more often than not is either the product of a geological phenomenon known as Triboluminescence, or as a consequence of a build up of Bioplasmic energy. First of all, the geological phenomenon of Triboluminescence is produced by friction of various crystals or similar minerals below ground level. This produces changes in the electromagnetic atmosphere at the location and may cause some individuals to hallucinate and experience 'seeing' apparitions. Triboluminescence somehow interferes with the electromagnetic atmosphere and precipitates images encapsulated in the Bioplasmic energy of the location. Powerful emotions produced by the human mind impregnate the subtle nature of an environment and help to create the personality of the psychic structure of bricks and mortar, making a building almost come 'alive'. In other words, not all ghostly apparitions are manifestations of so-called 'spirits of the dead!' More often than not they are no more than photographic images in the psychic space, and witnessing them is just like watching a monochrome video of an old movie. The psychic image phenomena is a display of often very clear apparitions that seem to have no awareness whatsoever of those who witness them. One example of such a phenomenon is one experienced by workmen excavating some Victorian sewers in Chester. While the group of men were busy renovating some dilapidated brickwork below Chester's most busy road, they were totally surprised to see a battalion of Roman soldiers marching through the wall, totally oblivious to their presence. The strange thing was, as the workmen observed the spectacular event, they noticed that the soldiers were only visible from their knees up. It was later discovered that the original road built by the Romans was in fact just below the level of the old sewer, and so, to the workmen it was just like watching a newsreel of past events. The Roman soldiers were Bioplasmic images captured in the environmental memory of time, and other similar sightings have been recorded at historical locations in various parts of Roman occupied Britain.

When trying to explain this phenomenon I always use the crude analogy of a video or audiotape, both of which are coated with a fine layer of a magnetic substance to enable both image and sound to be recorded. The ghostly apparition phenomenon is produced in the same way, when images of past events are impregnated into the electromagnetic atmosphere, they are permanently fixed in time. Of course, this particular phenomenon only accounts for a very small portion of paranormal phenomena, as most ghostly happenings are actual spirit manifestations and are produced by either inquisitive or unsettled spirits of the dead. When writing my Spooky Liverpool books, as well as telling an interesting story, it has also been my intention to help the reader explore all areas of paranormal phenomena so that he or she can have a much deeper understanding of exactly what happens when an apparition manifests at a haunted location. I have always maintained that the mind is the common denominator and, more often than not, paranormal experiences are subjective, and due to a 'short-circuit' in the brain. When a person is told that they are being taken to a haunted location, long before he or she arrives at their destination, the mind will have already created its own ghosts and demons, and whether the place is haunted or not, the imagination will have certainly taken over. On the other hand, should you not be privy to the paranormal background of a location you are visiting, you may find that nothing whatsoever is experienced. And so, we can see that the mind is very often the 'bridge' between the seen and the unseen, and between the real and the very unreal. In fact, the imagination often plays an integral part in paranormal experiences, and devout sceptics frequently lack this mental attribute – imagination, that is.

I have been working as a professional medium for over 25 years now, and I have always been considered somewhat radical and unconventional by my peers, primarily for my very sceptical approach to the subject. I have made an extensive study of all metaphysical and paranormal subjects, and although now somewhat of a cliché, I have no doubt whatsoever that 'there is most definitely far more to heaven and earth than meets the eye,' and if we are diligent we will always find what we are looking for. The problem I now have is the way in which a lot of people think it's quite fashionable to be involved with the paranormal. In fact, the paranormal has become big business, with self-styled paranormal investigators popping up everywhere – ghost hunters galore running 'Ghost Walks' and similar tourist attractions. Not to mention ghost story tellers who now seem to be considered as 'experts.' One ghost story writer, who previously dismissed mediums as charlatans, can now occasionally be heard on radio, demonstrating remote viewing. I'm expecting him to be giving demonstrations of clairvoyance next. The mind does boggle! This growing interest in the paranormal is primarily due to the way in which it is today presented on TV. In fact, you can now see mediums working on terrestrial channels, whereas before, because of the ITC regulations, mediums could only be seen demonstrating their abilities on Sky and Cable TV. Things have most certainly changed, and perhaps not for the better.

I have been personally involved in the majority of the paranormal cases in my books, and the rest have been extensively researched.

1

Sins of the Fathers

Barbara Jameson's 18-year-old son, Michael, had been murdered on his way home from a party. She knew she would never get over his untimely death, but she did hope that the pain would eventually get a little easier. At first the murder had placed an enormous strain on her marriage, but 10 years on Barbara's relationship with her husband, Peter, was much stronger than ever. Their only consolation was that Michael's murderer, Bob Carter, had been caught, prosecuted and given a life sentence.

The couple had moved into a new house in Moscow Drive, a couple of weeks before Christmas 1988, and now they both just wanted to put the past behind them. They had made their plans for the New Year and had already arranged for a local company to come and fit a new kitchen at the beginning of January. As far as the Jameson's were concerned, this was to be a new beginning.

Once the kitchen fitters had moved in, Barbara began to make arrangements for the new furniture to be delivered. She had decided that everything was going to be just perfect. Both Barbara and Peter had always been very particular about allowing workmen into their house, but the kitchen fitters were clean and polite and the couple trusted them. Whilst Peter was at work, Barbara supplied them with endless cups of tea. She found one of the young men particularly amiable and easy to talk to. During a conversation one morning, over a cup of tea and a biscuit, she asked him whether he was married. He told her that he had been married for five years and that his wife was expecting their second child in March.

'Do you have any other family?' she inquired. 'Are your parents still alive?'

The young man fell silent and appeared a little nervous.

'My mother died two years ago,' he said sadly. 'My father...' he suddenly stopped, moved in his seat and looked slightly uncomfortable. 'My father's erm... in prison.'

It was quite obvious that he did not want to speak about it any further and so Barbara decided to change the subject.

'You must be really excited about the baby,' she said. 'Not long to go now!'

But the young man appeared not to have heard her and muttered in a low voice. 'He murdered someone!'

'Who murdered someone?' asked Barbara. 'Your father?'

'Yes, it was horrible,' nodded the young man. 'He stabbed a young guy to death 10 years ago.'

A strange sensation washed over Barbara and for a moment she was unable to speak. She was not quite sure what the feeling was; she just knew that, as the young man spoke, his words had overwhelmed her.

'What is your father's name?' she asked, almost incoherently, somehow predicting exactly what the answer would be.

'Bob Carter,' came the reply. 'You won't know him. I wish I didn't know him either.'

'I know him alright,' snapped Barbara, her voice suddenly becoming cold and hard. 'He murdered my son, Michael Jameson. He was only 18.'

For a brief moment her eyes locked onto the young man's and all the sadness came rushing back. But then she realised that this was more than pure coincidence, that really there was no such thing as coincidence. She noted the anguish in the young man's eyes and in that moment she knew that all her pain was over. In this case, the sins of the father had truly been passed to the son.

She knew that it was not the young man's fault, and a slight smile parted her lips as she warmly touched his hand.

Billy says: This is one of life's extremely unexplainable coincidences that has perhaps been organised by a greater supernatural power, possibly to allow the ghost of things that have been to be laid to rest.

2

A Sojourn in the Past

We read so much about so-called 'Time slips', a phenomenon experienced by some people who claim that they found themselves somehow briefly transported in to the past. 'Retrospective viewing,' is the psychological phenomenon that causes the brain to somehow 'short circuit' so that the individual has an extremely vivid glimpse of the past, and may even find themselves in the same place but decades earlier. There have been numerous accounts of people experiencing this phenomenon in Bold Street, in Liverpool city centre, when they have claimed to have experienced 'Time slip,' and found themselves back in the 1950s. My story is somewhat different, and actually happened to someone I personally knew very well.

The year was 1966 and not only had the whole concept of music changed dramatically, almost over night, but the fashion scene had also seemingly gone crazy. Businessmen who had previously led fairly sedate lives were now growing their hair long and had exchanged their pinstripe suits for flared trousers and brightly coloured shirts. Psychedelic sounds could be heard on radios and jukeboxes everywhere, and although the whole of the world had seemingly been infected with the 60s fever, Liverpool had set the trend. The so-called Mersey beat boom had thrown an entire generation into a complete frenzy. The Beatles were preaching peace, love and transcendental meditation but, at the same time, young American soldiers were still dying in Vietnam.

Kevin Haines, however, was still living at home with his parents in their comfortable little semi-detached in Childwall. Although he had previously affirmed that at 18 there was still plenty of time to move into his own place, the sound of Jimi Hendrix's guitar had convinced him that it was now distinctly uncool to still be at home with the folks. Even in the 1960s, the Lark Lane area, around Sefton Park, was the place to be, and so Kevin and his girlfriend, Linda, moved into their first place together in Linnet Lane, much to the disapproval of his parents.

He soon decided that the move was the best thing he had ever done; producing an incredible metamorphosis of his whole life. His hair was now well over his collar and his previous, nicely groomed appearance had given way to faded and torn jeans, and a Kaftan and beads. As far as Kevin was concerned, he was now the coolest guy in town.

Kevin and Linda spent most of their spare time in O'Connor's Tavern in Hardman Street, and it was there, one Saturday night, that a friend encouraged him to take some mescaline. Both he and Linda had always been anti-drugs, and had both vowed never to experiment in any way whatsoever. However, this night was different, at least to Kevin, who looked upon it as a symbolic gesture, underlining his independence and the fact that he had become himself. Exactly what that meant, Kevin himself did not quite know, but at least it sounded good when he stood in O'Connor's and proclaimed it before his small circle of friends. As he vowed to Linda that this was the first and very last time, he swallowed the minute piece of impregnated paper, completely disregarding her earnest protestations.

An hour had passed by and now Kevin and Linda were sitting by the open fire at the end of the large room, discussing their plans for the future. Suddenly Kevin noticed that the cacophony of sounds, over which, only a few moments earlier, he had been forced to raise his voice in order to be heard, had diminished into nothingness. All that was left was silence and the slow movement of people passing by. Even Linda's voice had faded away completely, even though he could still see her lips moving. This was not what Kevin had expected from his first LSD trip, and the more he struggled to analyse what he was experiencing, the more he found himself unable to think at all. This, for some reason, made him smile. And very soon that smile turned into loud, uncontrollable laughter. Before long he was completely out of control, but was still somehow able to excuse himself whilst he clumsily negotiated his way to the toilets through the, by now, crowded pub.

Over half an hour had passed by and Kevin had still not returned from the toilet. Linda was naturally concerned and asked one of their mutual friends to go and investigate, but he was nowhere to be found. Feeling increasingly apprehensive, she eventually decided to make her way home alone and wait for him there. However, over the coming days and weeks, despite extensive police inquiries and appeals to other appropriate authorities, Kevin could not be traced.

Just over a year later Linda was in the kitchen of her flat, preparing herself a snack before setting out to visit her mother in West Derby. As she worked she was singing along to the music blaring out from the radio in the living room, so she failed to hear the commotion at the front door. It was only when she entered the living room to turn the radio down that she saw, to her amazement that Kevin was walking through the door. She froze, speechless for a few moments, as he walked towards her, smiling, as though nothing had happened.

'Kevin!' she eventually managed to gasp. 'Where on earth...?'

She stopped mid-sentence, as she eyed him from head to toe. Although Kevin had been missing for 13 months, he looked exactly the same as he had done on that night in O'Connor's Tavern, before he had disappeared without trace. His hair was exactly the same length and he was still wearing the same clothes. Linda, however, had changed completely. Her hair was now short, and she had lost a great deal of weight, due to all the stress of Kevin's disappearance. She simply could not believe what she was seeing and could not decide whether to throw her arms around him or to slap him hard across the face. He stood directly in front of her, grinning nervously, and she suddenly realised that something was very wrong.

'Where have you been?' she asked him anxiously. 'Why didn't you get in touch?'

Kevin's smile faded and he suddenly looked deathly pale as he lowered himself wearily onto the settee.

'You won't believe me when I tell you,' he said, his voice sounding weak and tired.

'Try me,' urged Linda, joining him on the settee, all the time unable to take her eyes off him. Her voice became softer as it gradually became more apparent that there was something very wrong, and that he hadn't disappeared through any fault of his own. 'What happened?'

'I went into the toilet feeling quite ill,' he began, 'and when I eventually came out of the cubicle, everywhere looked so different.'

'Different?' said Linda. 'What do you mean?'

'I was in a different place. I didn't have a clue where I was until someone came into the room.' He paused for a moment and rubbed his brow, as if trying desperately to make sense of the memory. 'The man was dressed in Victorian clothes. For a moment I thought he had been to a fancy dress party. It wasn't until I went to look for you that I realised I had somehow travelled back in time. Everyone was dressed in Victorian clothes.' He stopped and looked at Linda, searching her face for some sort of response. 'I know it all sounds crazy. A young woman approached me and called me Douglas. Her name was Clare. Apparently she was my sister. I didn't know what to say, and so I decided to be guided by her. She asked me if I was feeling better and then she called a carriage and took me home.'

Linda listened to the whole story with keen interest and, although she found it extremely far-fetched, there was something about Kevin's demeanour, which made it quite convincing. He concluded by telling her that his name had been Douglas Smothers, a historian living in Allerton.

'I died of consumption at the age of 35,' he said, without a trace of irony. 'I was buried in Smithdown Road Cemetery.'

Linda immediately realised that this information could quite easily be substantiated, simply by visiting the grave, so its existence did not really prove anything at all. Kevin could have seen the grave and used the details on the headstone to elaborate his incredible story. However, the following day, Kevin took Linda to the grave, which was just where he had said they would find it, In Smithdown Road Cemetery. She was completely baffled by the whole plausible account, and was still sceptical about its authenticity. However, there were more revelations to come.

Over the following months, Kevin began to surprise everyone with his accurate historical knowledge of Great Britain and, in particular, of the period covering the reign of Queen Victoria. Before his disappearance, Kevin had never shown any interest in history, a fact that was clearly reflected in his school reports. His knowledge was now quite extensive and it soon became obvious that he intended to use it in his career. Within two years, Kevin Haines had developed a reputation for being an authority on Victorian England and was often consulted by film companies and TV corporations.

His life had been transformed in more ways than one. In 1979 he even took the drastic step of changing his name by deed poll to Douglas Smothers. Although this is a true story, the names have been changed for obvious reasons. I must stress that it is not my intention to in any way glorify the use of lysergic acid, as I have known it to destroy the minds of many users.

Billy says: Kevin's experience is definitely an isolated case, in which the hallucinogenic drug mescaline precipitated the full potential of his mind and must have somehow connected him to a previous life in another time. Was this really a case for Reincarnation?

3

Encounters in the Cemetery

Since Jack Postlethwaite had died after a short illness 12 months ago, his wife Sarah had visited his grave in Anfield Cemetery every Sunday, hail rain or snow, without fail. Just tidying the grave and talking to her dead husband gave her some comfort, and although she had two loving daughters, Sarah was only too aware that they had their own lives to live, and now she had to make the best of hers, unfortunately without her husband, Jack. When the weather was good, Sarah would sometimes take a flask of tea and some sandwiches and sit by the grave on her husband's fishing chair that she always kept in the car, chatting away and telling him how her week had been. She was certain he could hear her, and it was only this comforting thought that kept her going. On each occasion she had visited the cemetery she had noticed an elderly man standing over a grave a few rows away, staring sadly into space. Obviously missing his wife, Sarah had assumed, and although she frequently tried to engage the well-dressed man in conversation, he always seemed far too wrapped up in his own grief to even pass her the time of day. Sarah had always been the talkative type, and would talk to anyone, her husband always said. Even her daughters had always warned her about talking to strangers, 'especially in the cemetery, mother.' Sarah always dismissed their worries, maintaining that she was now far too old to change, and that it costs nothing to offer a kindly word to a person in need. One beautiful autumnal Sunday afternoon, Sarah decided to pass the time of day to the gentleman, and although he appeared reluctant to engage in conversation, Sarah's persistence gave him no alternative but to speak.

'I'm worried about my wife,' he lamented almost incoherently. 'Do you think she'll be alright?'

Sarah lowered her eyes to the sparse grave, noting the absence of any head stone or plaque bearing his wife's name; just a bunch of red roses representing his love.

'Of course she'll be alright.' Sarah reassured him warmly. 'God is good and always takes care of his own.' She looked sympathetically at the sadness in the gentleman's eyes, and the pained expression on his face brought back her own grief when her husband, Jack, had died. She placed a comforting hand on the man's shoulder and noticed he felt cold. 'You'll catch your death here,' she said. 'Would you like a cup of tea to warm you? I've got a flask full.'

The gentleman seemed to ignore Sarah and just continued to stare sadly at the grave.

'My name's Sarah,' she said, trying desperately to break the heavy silence, and making every effort to put the man at ease. 'What's your name?'

'Ted.' He mumbled. 'My wife's name is Irene.'

'The pain will ease in time,' she continued. 'Believe me, I know.' The man turned to face Sarah, and a half smile slightly parted his lips.

'Thank you,' he said quietly. 'You are kind.' He then turned and walked away without saying another word. Sarah watched him for a few moments before returning to her husband's grave.

All week Sarah found the gentleman constantly coming into her thoughts, and she just hoped that she had helped him a little with what she had said. The following Sunday, as usual, she made her way to the cemetery, making sure that she'd packed an extra cup and a few more sandwiches than usual, in the hope of encouraging the gentleman to join her. It was a bright, clear day, and the cemetery was busier than usual, but there was no sign of the man at all. Instead Sarah noticed an elderly lady and a young woman standing at the grave, which to her surprise now had a new marble headstone. The two women we standing there proudly inspecting the new gravestone, and Sarah called, 'It looks so much better now, doesn't it?'

The young woman looked at Sarah and smiled. 'Yes, we're very pleased.' Sarah couldn't help but notice that the older of the two women looked quite despondent, and so after securing her husband's chair in its usual place close to the grave, she walked over to have a closer look at the newly fitted gravestone.

'My name's Sarah - Sarah Postlethwaite'. She said. 'I visit my husband's grave every Sunday without fail. It's so quiet and peaceful here.'

The oldest woman looked at Sarah. 'Yes, it is. My name is Irene, and this is my daughter Barbara.'

'Irene?' repeated Sarah quizzically, moving her eyes slowly to the grave. 'You must be...' she stuttered, searching for the words whilst her eyes read the newly engraved inscription on the new headstone.

'Ted's wife,' interrupted the woman, nodding sadly at the grave. 'This is my husband's grave. He died six months ago.'

'But...' Sarah stuttered again. 'I...'

'You what?' asked the woman's daughter.

Sarah paused for a moment before allowing a smile to break across her lips. 'Oh, nothing,' she answered. 'I must have been mistaken.'

The Vanishing Little Girl

Contrary to popular belief, a cemetery is the last place in which I would expect a so-called 'ghost' to be seen. Even so, there are innumerable accounts of ghostly appearances in cemeteries. Several people have related their stories of the vanishing little girl in Anfield Cemetery. One sunny afternoon whilst on their way to her husband's grave, Margaret Fowler and her daughter Jane came face to face with a slightly built little girl of around the age of nine, who stood in front of them smiling, before disappearing completely. The young girl had walked between the gravestones and had lingered for a few moments by a grave with nothing more than a leaning marble cross to mark its position. The grave was overgrown, and looked as though nobody had visited it for years. On closer inspection, Jane read the inscription on the cross. 'Our Becky, tragically taken from us at the age of nine.' They both felt an icy shiver pass through them, and were overwhelmed with sadness, when they realised that they had come face to face with Becky, the smiling little girl.

A Double Take

The phenomenon of 'Spirit Extras' on photographs has for many years been the subject of paranormal debate. Unfortunately, once under scientific scrutiny many of these have been dismissed as 'fakes.' However, since the development of the digital camera, faking photographic ghostly images is virtually impossible, and so I am always excited when I receive a photograph with a clear image of a so-called 'Spirit Extra', particularly when the image has been identified as a deceased member of the family.

The tragic death of 27-year-old Debbie Watts, devastated her husband of nine months. The couple had not long had their first child when she was diagnosed with breast cancer. Although the initial prognosis had been promising, the disease quickly spread and the young mother sadly died within four months.

It was a fairly blustery and yet sunny day and Debbie's sister, Sharon, and her husband, John, had gone to see the newly laid headstone and to place some flowers on the grave. Before they left, Sharon took several photographs of the new gravestone to show her mother who was at home recovering from a painful bout of sciatica. After running them through his computer, John carefully inspected one of the photographs with amazement. He called his wife excitedly to come and have a look at the photograph. Although four of the photographs had been taken from exactly the same position, on one of the photographs the unmistakable ghostly form of Debbie could be clearly seen standing behind her own grave, smiling cheerfully at the camera. Although the family still missed Debbie very much, at least they now knew that she was happy, and they had the photograph of her to prove it.

Billy says: Although photographs of this nature are extremely rare, they do prove that our deceased loved ones occasionally make the effort to tell us that they are still alive. Sometimes their 'Spirit Image' is seen transfiguring round an object, such as a chair or even an ornament. The face of a deceased person can also be seen in a pattern on curtains or even wallpaper. Once seen, never forgotten! I did have a photograph of the above phenomenon, but as it was taken on a mobile phone the quality was too poor to reproduce.

The Gatekeeper of Toxteth Cemetery

Through the years there have been numerous accounts of ghostly Gate Keepers, usually seen at the gates of cemeteries, seemingly keeping vigil over those who silently sleep in the graveyard. Some of the stories are quite difficult to believe, but they still send an icy chill down the spine.

It was 1964 and Graham Peters and his wife, Rosy, had lived in their two bedroom flat in Sydenham Avenue, off Ullet Road and Arundel Avenue, for just over two weeks. They had both decided that this was a new beginning for them, and were putting their spate of bad luck behind them. They desperately wanted to start a family, but Rosy had miscarried three times, and now the couple were both feeling very despondent. Rosy had studied interior design at college, and so she had already decided upon the colour scheme and how everything would be arranged in the flat. This at least took her mind off their problems, and Rosy hoped that without the added pressure, she might just become pregnant again. Graham's mother had insisted that the couple should come every Friday for tea, and although they were very busy painting and hanging wallpaper, they did not want to disappoint her.

As neither of the couple could drive, they always took a shortcut through the turnstile into Toxteth Cemetery, which led directly to Smithdown Road. Graham's mother lived alone in Abyssinia Street, just off Wellington Road, and so cutting through the cemetery meant that they could make the journey walking to his mother's house, in half an hour.

It was late autumn and the dark nights were well and truly on their way. The turnstile gate in the high sandstone wall, at the other side of the cemetery, was usually locked at nightfall, and so the couple made their excuses and began their journey home. By this time it was very cold and the cemetery deserted. It was an eerie place at the best of times, but as soon as nightfall came, it seemed to be much darker in the cemetery than anywhere else. Rosy clung onto Graham's arm as they made their way through the cemetery. They had reached the other side in no time at all, and Graham thought he could see someone standing by the gate. 'Perhaps it's the man locking the gate?' suggested Rosy, with an urgent tone. 'We'd better hurry.'

When the couple were only yards away from the turnstile, they stopped, unable to believe their eyes. The glowing cloaked figure of man stood by the gate, his arms folded in front of him as he looked towards them. 'Who the hell's that?' muttered Graham, disbelievingly, wondering at the same time if they should turn back. For a moment it seemed as though time had stood still, as the couple watched the figure. Suddenly, the brightly glowing hooded phantom, beckoned for them to pass through the turnstile, before turning to walk off into the darkness.

'What the hell was that?' gasped Rosy, pulling her husband towards the turnstile gate. 'Let's go before he comes back.'

They made a hasty retreat from the cemetery, but sat up talking about the hooded phantom for hours. Two days later, Rosy received a phone call from her doctor. 'I've got the results of your pregnancy test,' said the voice at the other end of the phone. 'You're pregnant! Congratulations.'

Nine months later Rosy gave birth to a little girl. Although they were both certain that the ghostly gatekeeper had something to do with it, they never walked through the cemetery ever again.

The ghostly gatekeeper in Toxteth Cemetery (or Smithdown Road Cemetery, as some know it) has been seen by many people over the years. Who he is, nobody knows. However, one thing is certain, those who see him really do benefit in some way from his appearance.

The Gatekeeper of Anfield Cemetery

Although it's comforting to think that a ghostly gatekeeper is watching over the cemeteries where our loved ones lie, it is nonetheless still quite spine chilling. Despite always adopting the policy, 'seeing is believing', there are far too many stories of ghostly gatekeepers for them not to be true. In the 1940s and 50s there were innumerable reports of a monastic ghostly figure, with a cowl covered head, seen in Anfield Cemetery, walking between the graves. The spooky phantom was nearly always seen at the Cherry Lane side of the cemetery, and when confronted, just disappeared into thin air. Sometimes only the cowl-covered head could be seen floating over the gravestones, restless and menacing, as though searching for something or, someone...

4

The Ghostly Goings on at Rigby's Pub

I first visited Rigby's Public House in Dale Street with Daily Post journalist, Mike Chapple, three years ago, when we conducted a 'Haunted pub' crawl (any excuse, Mike!). There had been many sightings of an 18th century coachman and other ghostly visitors in the pub late at night, and Fiona Watkin, the landlady of the very atmospheric hostelry, invited us, after hours, to see if I could 'home-in', so to speak, to the disembodied visitors. Although I have been a professional medium for over 25 years, I am probably one of the most sceptical mediums in my profession, and I have always adopted the very healthy attitude of 'seeing is really believing', especially if you want to avoid disappointment. The name Rigby's is derived from local politician and publican, Thomas Rigby, who had the pub from 1852 until the day he died in 1886. He is believed to have died in the pub, and he is most probably one of the ghostly visitors seen there by some people.

By the time we arrived just after midnight, the pub was already closed and locked up, and Fiona met us outside. When she unlocked the door and led us inside, I was immediately overwhelmed with a strong feeling of foreboding, and felt very strongly as though an invisible hand was preventing me from entering. That may sound a little crazy to some people, but that's the way some haunted locations affect me. I felt very apprehensive that night and knew almost immediately that we would experience something. Although I don't need 'ghost busting' gadgets, popularised by the TV programme Most Haunted, I took with me an EMF (Electromagnetic Frequency) meter and a non-contact thermometer. The EMF meter helps to monitor any remarkable changes in the electromagnetic atmosphere, quite common when there is any sort of paranormal activity. I was also armed with a non-contact thermometer and laser, a useful device for monitoring temperature changes, also quite usual when there is a 'ghostly presence.' The laser beam enables the device to register the temperature on the far side of the room, without even being there. Also, should any invisible force pass through the laser beam, the broken contact registers on the gauge. So, all in all, both devices are quite interesting, and make very effective visual aids. I also expect a building as old as Rigby's to have some sort of paranormal atmosphere. After all, it has been frequented by thousands of people over the past few hundreds years, and on the night I was certain something was going to happen. We had only been in the building for 20 minutes, when I became aware of the ghostly figure of a very diminutive balding man, dressed in breeches and a frock coat. What hair he did have was pulled tightly back into a short ponytail. He seemed to be following us around the pub, grinning with delight that I could actually 'see' him. The EMF Meter went crazy, and although it was quite warm in the pub, the temperature on the hand held non-contact thermometer dropped considerably. Although I did not think our ghostly visitor was in anyway malevolent, I could see that he was mischievous with an incredible sense of humour. I also encountered a very overweight lady with a long dress and white apron, and her head piled into a bun on the top of her head. Now, she looked quite malevolent, and I remarked to myself that I would not like to spend the night there alone with her! She seemed to be angry, and was probably one of the ghostly culprits responsible for kicking some of Rigby's staff while they have been working. In fact, Tommy Rockliffe, Rigby's chef, has seen plates and other items thrown into the air, and has witnessed other poltergeist activity in the kitchen. The atmosphere in Rigby's changes constantly, indicative of a location with a lot of paranormal activity. Although there is no

documented evidence to support it, Admiral Lord Nelson is believed to have taken a drink there occasionally. Whether or not that story is true, the quiet corner in which he allegedly raised his tankard is today called 'Nelson's Room', a tribute to one of England's finest historical figures. Who knows, Nelson might just sit next to you next time you pop into Rigbys for a quick one!

Some months ago I received a photograph from a young lady who had taken some friends to Rigby's for a drink. Sitting behind the two young ladies in the photograph, as clear as anything, is seen the ghostly image of the coachman I had seen when I visited Rigby's. I was absolutely amazed. Rigby's landlady, Fiona, has seen the ghostly coachman on many occasions. Now we have a photograph of the jolly man, who seems to delight in having his photograph taken.

Billy says: Should you be interested in the ghostly goings on in Liverpool, I would certainly recommend a visit to Rigby's in Dale Street. Apart from everything else, there is a pleasant atmosphere and, more importantly, the wine is good!

The Ghosts of Ye Hole in Ye Wall

Ye Hole In Ye Wall, a quaint little pub located in Hackins Hey, off Dale Street, in Liverpool city centre, has been a hostelry since 1726. Liverpool was then a growing port, visited by ships from all over the world. Ye Hole In Ye Wall is perhaps overlooked by storytellers when relating ghostly tales of pubs around Liverpool, and yet even this friendly hostelry has a story to tell.

In Victorian times, when press-ganging was still usual practise, particularly in the port of Liverpool, a Spanish seafarer was waylaid whilst he was having a quiet drink with friends in Ye Hole In Ye Wall, and when he put up a fight, he was stabbed and beaten to death before many eye-witnesses. What is purported to be the Spanish sailor's ghost has been seen on many occasions in Ye Hole In Ye Wall. Those who have glimpsed the ghostly figure say that he looks bewildered and lost. The trauma experienced by the sailor has obviously made an incredibly great impact on the psychic atmosphere of the pub, and the 'dead' Spanish sailor is making sure that his untimely death is never forgotten.

As I have previously said, old buildings and locations have memories the same as people. Nothing is ever forgotten, no word ever spoken is ever lost. Both joy and sadness reverberate through time, ensuring that those who pass by never forget...

An extremely tall, ghostly figure with a cowl-covered head has always been seen in and around Ye Hole In Ye Wall, allegedly one of an elite sect of monks who lived on the banks of the Dee Estuary over 400 years ago. These unusually tall monastic figures were believed to be quite radical and very fierce. However, whether or not this is true nobody can confirm.

5

Apparition in Holy Trinity

Holy Trinity Cemetery overlooks Wavertree Park, or 'The Mystery' as it is known locally. In fact, people frequently use it as a short cut to get to Church Road from Grant Avenue and, apart from this, Holy Trinity is just like any other cemetery. May Rogers had visited Holy Trinity every Sunday since her mother had died five years before, and had always found it to be quite peaceful. Her eight-year-old son, Michael, always accompanied her, and would always amuse himself whilst his mother tidied the grave and then fetched water from the nearby tap, before arranging the flowers in the pot. Although Michael always found the trip to the cemetery boring, it was a weekly ritual he put up with for his mother's sake. It was March 1990 and, because Michael was going to his cousin's birthday party, they had gone to the cemetery in the morning, instead of the usual time in the afternoon. As soon as they arrived at the cemetery Michael's mother quickly set about tidying the grave, and Michael went to fetch the water for the flowers. Whilst he was filling the pot with water he noticed a lady standing beside him, waiting to use the tap, he thought. She smiled at him, 'Hello Michael,' she said warmly. 'You've grown into a fine young man, haven't you?' Thinking that she was someone who knew his mother, he smiled politely back at her, and then turned to make his way back to the grave. 'Michael,' the woman said, holding out her hand to him. 'Give your mother this, she lost it.' Michael held out his hand, and the woman dropped a gold ring into his palm. He closed his fingers tightly around the wedding ring, thanked the lady, and then made his way back to his mother.

'Where have you been?' she asked, shaking her head impatiently. 'I've been waiting for the water.'

'I've been speaking to a nice lady,' he said, holding out the ring to his mother. 'She said to give you this, that you'd lost it.'

Her eyes widened as she took the ring from her son. She examined it closely, mouthing the worn inscription inside the gold band. 'Ron and Margaret - 12. 4. 41.' She couldn't believe that she was actually holding her mother's wedding ring in her hand. It had been left on her mother's hand and buried with her. She had often wished that she had kept it, just as her mother had wanted. But Ron, her older brother had insisted that it be left on his mother's hand. She swung round to see the lady her son had been speaking to, but there was nobody there.

'She was there, honest, mum,' Michael insisted. 'She did give me the ring.'

May could see that her son was quite upset, and so she placed a reassuring hand on his head. 'I know, son. I know.'

She smiled to herself, and felt an icy-cold shiver pass right through her, as she lowered her eyes to her mother's grave. 'Thanks mum,' she whispered. 'I love you.'

6

THE SOUTHPORT POLTERGEIST

I am frequently asked if anything ever frightens me, and if I'm perfectly honest lots of things terrify me. For one thing I do not like being confronted with the unknown, and I do like to be prepared at all times. Although I have studied the occult for more than 30 years, I am always reluctant to accept invitations to visit haunted locations, until, that is, I have had time to explore the whole paranormal story and know exactly what it is I am letting myself in for. Only then can I truly give my best and feel confident that I can help resolve the paranormal predicament. I have always had a particular interest in the poltergeist phenomenon, and always felt quite excited when I receive an invitation to investigate one. As I discussed in my first Spooky Liverpool book, I always use the word 'poltergeist' as an umbrella term to cover a broad spectrum of paranormal phenomena. To me, the movement of objects by a seemingly disembodied source does not always suggest the manifestation of a poltergeist. Telekinetic activity (the movement of solid objects) may be caused by numerous natural phenomena, such as geological faults, or even electrical interference that somehow interrupts the electro-magnetic atmosphere. I have to say that this was the most frightening experience I have ever had during my life as a professional medium.

The man's voice at the end of the phone sounded quite nervous; almost reluctant to speak. 'I was given your number by a friend,' he said, coughing nervously to clear his throat. 'I was wondering if you could help me?'

After a few minutes of conversation, the man explained that he owned a Victorian house in Southport, and that because of some 'unusual goings on,' he was having some difficulty selling. 'It's been on the market for two years now. I would appreciate it if you could come and take a look. Don't mind paying for your time.'

The man explained that a previously invited medium had in fact been violently sick, and simply refused to return to the house. This immediately sent alarm bells ringing loudly in my head, and my first reaction was to decline the invitation. However, after giving it some thought I agreed to visit the house a few days later. Upon arriving at the magnificent old building, I sat in the car for a few moments and tried desperately to compose myself before going in to God knows what. To be quite honest I had never felt so nervous, and the anticipation caused my heart to beat so rapidly inside my chest that I felt I couldn't breathe. The well-dressed man must have been watching me from the window as the ornate front door was opened even before my hand had reached the tarnished heavy brass knocker.

The garden was extremely overgrown with upturned oil drums, dismantled car parts and other rubbish strewn all over the place. As soon as I entered the hallway I was immediately overwhelmed with the pungent smell of damp and other fragrances usually associated with empty houses. It was clear that the grand old house had been quite magnificent in its day, and had obviously been the home to a wealthy Victorian trader or well-to-do family. The impressive broad staircase still retained some of its dignity as it gradually wound its way up and then spread beneath a beautiful leaded window on the landing above. The leaded flowers on the window were still intact, and the daylight filtered through the grimy glass and cast an eerie shadow down the stairs. In fact, it was an ideal setting for a Hammer House of Horror movie, complete with its eerie sounds and moving shadows. Although the owner of the house was keen for me to take a look in the down stairs rooms, I was somehow immediately drawn up the stairs to the landing beneath the leaded window. He left me to my own devices and allowed me to follow my gaze up the stairs, mesmerised by the light filtering through the different coloured glass on the window. I had no sooner reached the first landing under the window, than I was again overwhelmed with a pungent smell. This time though it was like rotting cabbage, and I could hear a piercing hissing sound, rather like faulty water pipes in an old house. I was extremely nervous and constantly looked over my shoulder. It was a strange feeling, and although I could hear the owner of the house moving things around somewhere downstairs, I was still very nervous. In fact, the more nervous I became the more I could feel an overwhelming pressure in the surrounding air. I could feel the hairs stand up on the back of my neck, and I was overwhelmed with a feeling of disorientation. I tried to ignore this and stood for a few moments on the landing, admiring the beautiful leaded window, and allowing my thoughts to drift back to the days when the house was inhabited by the wealthy trader. I suddenly heard a creaking sound and turned to see a blue vase standing on a small table in the corner, vibrating fiercely for no reason whatsoever. I watched intently as it suddenly flew off the table and landed gently in an upright position on the floor. The table carried on vibrating and some unseen force took my by the shoulders and violently swung me round to face the wall. I felt an icy chill pass right through me, and then without any warning at all, I was lifted two or three inches from the floor and thrown with great force against the wall. Although all this took place in no more than one minute, I was terrified and could feel my heart beating inside my chest. I felt as though I had a huge ball in the pit of my stomach and had to run quickly down the stairs to vomit in the front garden. Having heard the commotion, the owner of the house came to investigate. When he saw what state I was in he confessed that exactly the same thing happened to a previously invited medium. For reason best known to himself he had seen fit not to disclose this bit of information to me. 'I desperately needed you to come,' he said, almost apologetically. 'I was told that if anyone could help me it would be you.'

I sat on the step until I had fully recovered from the very strange and frightening ordeal, and then decided to go back inside and face whatever it was again. I had always been taught not to allow any paranormal force to overcome me, and that fear itself empowers any negative supernatural energy. Once inside the house I moved quickly from room to room, at all times aware of 'something' following me as I wended my way along the narrow landing and up the attic staircase leading to three rooms in the apex of the house. Something made me stop outside one of the doors, and I was certain that this was the epicentre of all the paranormal chaos. I felt extremely cold and yet my hands were clammy; my heart was racing with the anticipation as I slowly pushed open the door and reluctantly entered the room. I was again overwhelmed with the same foul smell that had hit me when I first entered the house. Things were happening in my peripheral vision, and when I swung my head round to see what it was, the room was completely empty. I walked further into the room and the creaking of the door, as it slammed shut behind me, made me jump out of my skin. It was like watching a late night horror movie, only this was real and I was actually there. If I'm perfectly honest I wanted to be anywhere but there. I could feel my stomach turning over and my whole body shaking. As I turned to make my way to the door an ashen-faced elderly man with menacing eyes confronted me. Although I knew that he was a 'ghost', I found myself unable to move forward. At first his nebulous spirit form pulsated weakly beneath the dim light filtering through the grimy window, just like the poor reception of a TV, but then he became clear and tangible. He appeared to be very angry and told me he had committed suicide by hanging himself from the staircase. He disappeared as quickly as he had appeared. Needless to say I made a hasty retreat and did not stop until I had reached the hallway by the front door.

When my sojourn in the very disturbed Victorian house had come to an end, I concluded that there were in fact several very different discarnate energies, all of which had contributed to the paranormal havoc. One elderly lady who had obviously lived in the house, had been ill for many years, and the misery she had experienced had become an integral part of the subtle personality of the physical structure of the house itself. I had to admit to the owner of the house that this was all beyond me. 'You will sell the house to a German businessman,' I predicted. 'But he will demolish it.'

Some years later I met the owner of the house and he confirmed that my prediction had in fact come true. The interesting thing is, a haunted house can be demolished, but the paranormal activity will persist, regardless of what is built in its place. Whatever is built there now will surely experience similar phenomena. In fact, a Rest Home for the elderly now stands on that very site.

Billy says: The Victorian house was situated very close to where the famous Palace Hotel used to stand. I have found the entire area situated on a network of Ley Lines that may also be responsible for a lot of paranormal activity experienced by many of the location's inhabitants.

7

The Mystery of the Palace Hotel

Most people are familiar with the story of the Palace Hotel, in Southport, a magnificent example of Victorian architecture, designed by William Magnall and built in 1866. At this time Southport was a thriving Victorian seaside resort, frequented by holidaymakers from all over the world. It was believed that there was 'something' in the air that was effective in aiding the recovery from consumption and other respiratory diseases, which was also the reason why Southport had a large sanatorium, now apartments, situated overlooking the Marina. In those days Southport had everything, with one of the most visited beaches in the country.

On the completion of the Palace Hotel, the architect discovered that it had in fact been built facing the opposite way to his design. Although for many years it was believed that Magnall had committed suicide by throwing himself from the roof of the hotel, supposedly in a demonstration of his displeasure as to the way it had been built, there is some evidence to suggest that this was untrue, and that he did in fact die of consumption, two years after the hotel was actually completed. Nonetheless, Southport's Palace Hotel was allegedly the epicentre for innumerable paranormal phenomena, which it is believed led to its ultimate demise and closure in 1967. Phyllis Broadbent, now in her late-eighties, told me that her grandmother worked in the hotel as a chambermaid, from the very day it opened its doors, and remembers her reminiscing about all the famous people who stayed in the hotel. She claimed to have even met Charles Dickens who stayed there for one night, sometime in 1868, two years before he died. Phyllis's grandmother, Alice, frequently stayed in the hotel, and bore witness to many 'odd' goings on in some of the rooms. She told her granddaughter that she had once met a tall, well-dressed gentleman in one of the corridors, who politely raised his hat to her before finally disappearing right in front of her. She had also heard disembodied cries echoing down the corridors late at night, and in some of the rooms lights would turn on and off by themselves. Many of the staff were too afraid to walk unaccompanied down the corridors at night, and some even left there jobs simply because they found it all too scary to work there.

The Palace Hotel was in fact used as the location for many films, including The Sorcerer, starring Boris Karloff, and boasted famous guests such as Frank Sinatra, Clark Gable, and the infamous couple Florence and James Maybrick, to name but a few.

Even when the hotel closed its doors for business, the lifts were frequently seen moving up and down of their own accord, even when they were not connected to any power source. The hotel was eventually demolished, and today all that remains of it is the Fishermens Rest Public House, which was once the coach house and stables.

8

Evil Goings on in the Basement

Although once a busy shopping area, Smithdown Road never really recovered from the Second World War. By the 1960s, the shops around the top part, from the cemetery all the way to the junction where Smithdown Road meets Lodge Lane, Earle Road and Upper Parliament Street, businesses were falling into disrepair and closing down. By 1970 shops that once sold respectable goods ranging from fashionable clothes to electrical merchandise and even motorbikes, were now selling second hand furniture, used washing machines and cookers, and even these shops did not survive longer than 12 months. One corner shop, almost opposite Hartington Road, had been empty and boarded up for more than two years, and for some reason best known to the owners of the property, it was left in this state without any attempt to refurbish it. Sometime in the early 1970s developers moved in and began extensively refurbishing the property. The workmen were certainly not prepared for the macabre scene they were to discover in the basement. A meticulously designed pentagram filled the entire floor space, and the black walls were daubed with human blood and body parts. On further investigation the workmen discovered the remains of animals and the dismembered remains of a newly born baby, obviously left over from a black mass ritual. Work was immediately suspended and the police called in. Once their lengthy investigations were concluded, the property was boarded up again and remained this way for some years. Although today most people have forgotten the macabre scenario, a dark cloud still looms heavily over the corner shop, and casts an even bigger and more grisly shadow over the whole community.

9

The Ghosts of Churches

ST NICHOLAS' CHURCH

Having been christened in St Nicholas' church, my father always spoke of it with great fondness. Although he was quite sceptical about the supernatural, he was still a mine of information regarding haunted locations around Liverpool.

There is believed to have been a place of worship on the site of Our Lady and St Nicholas' Church since approximately 1257. The church is close to the River Mersey, and St Nicholas is the patron saint of sailors. However, the present church was built on the site of St Mary Del Quay.

On Sunday, February 11, 1810, as the bells tolled and people were gathering for the morning service, the tower of St Nicholas dislodged and crashed to the ground, killing 25 children and three adults. The sound of crashing timber and masonry, followed by screaming disembodied voices has been heard on the anniversary of the disaster, and some witnesses have claimed to have seen the ghostly figures of children on the spot where it took place. As a young boy my father and his mother saw a 'replay' of the disaster, and both stood in sheer horror as they listened to ghostly cries of children. 'It was like being at the pictures,' remarked my father nostalgically. 'Other people passing by also witnessed it.'

St Nicholas' Church seems to be the epicentre for other

paranormal sightings. The ghost of Ned Fallows has also been seen in the early hours of the morning. In 1830, the young seafarer's ship had docked and he was making his way to his home in Everton in the early hours of the morning, when he was beaten to death and robbed of one guinea and some tobacco. The perpetrators of the crime were caught and hanged, but the ghostly form of young Ned Fallows is frequently seen still making his way home.

Also, when the dashing Prince Rupert attacked Liverpool, prisoners were kept in St Nicholas' Chapel whilst the battle raged on. Little wonder then that this fine old church possesses more ghostly memories than most!

Billy says: This phenomenon is quite common, and is often no more than a 'ghostly replay' of the sad event, a sort of a photographic image in the psychic atmosphere.

ST HUGH'S (IN LAWRENCE ROAD) THE DISAPPEARING LADY

Given the amount of emotion and anguish that has been released in all churches through the years, one would expect that they would all have their ghosts of one kind or another. Occasionally, though, ghostly appearances happen for a particular reason. Some years ago now, I was experiencing a particularly difficult time. I was on the brink of despair and frequently found solace just sitting quietly in a church. Unfortunately, because of vandalism today churches are rarely found open. St Hugh's is on Lawrence Road in Wavertree, not far from where I lived in Grosvenor Road. I wandered into the church and sat somewhere around the middle, from where I had a very clear view of the altar. I have always believed in the power of prayer and have always integrated this somehow into my daily life. I had just finished praying, and had lowered my head to my chest, when I was overcome with emotion. The more I tried to stifle my sobs, the more they echoed around the empty church. At this point nobody had entered the church, and there was certainly nobody praying in front of the altar. But, someone crying suddenly caught my attention. I raised my head to see the diminutive figure of an old lady praying on her knees in front of the altar. She pulled herself tiredly to her feet, made the sign of the cross, and then turned to make her way down the aisle and past me. She was wearing a well-worn coat, and had a floral coloured scarf pulled about her head, framing her pale and very lined face. For a brief moment her sad eyes met mine, and a slight smile parted her thin lips. I turned to watch her as she walked by – but she had gone – disappeared into thin air. My heart missed several beats, and I stood up to make certain that she was not there. A sweet fragrance wafted over me, and I could feel an icy chill pass through my body. Whoever the lady was, she certainly appeared to me for a reason, and most certainly made me realise that I was not the only one in the world who felt sad. I smiled to myself, and left the church feeling much better than when I had entered it.

10

Ghosts of Old Hall Street

In May 1644, Prince Rupert attacked the town hall of Liverpool, then known as Liverpul. His troops were stationed on the hills overlooking the town (such as Beacon Hill in Everton, and Copperas Hill.) On June 13 his soldiers forced their way into the north, around what is known today as Old Hall Street, but known then as Peppard Street and also Whiteacre Street. The Parliamentary Troops, under the leadership of John Moore, had fled Liverpool, without informing the town's citizens, and leaving them to fend for themselves. Although the people of Liverpool are believed to have put up a courageous fight, they were no match for Prince Rupert's professional soldiers, who charged in and slaughtered all those who put up a resistance. The entire area was a veritable blood bath, with the streets strewn with bodies.

The Moore family's house was called Moore Hall, and when they moved to Bank Hall, they always referred to their home as the 'Old Hall', the primary reason for the street leading to it became known as Old Hall Street.

On July 2 the Battle of Marston Moor took place, and not long after this the Parliamentary troops regained control of Liverpool. The scene of the battle was reduced to rubble, and once again there were hundreds of mortalities.

Although by day, Old Hall Street is an extremely busy area, by night you would be warned to take great care when walking down it alone. Many have said that they have heard the disembodied cries of men being slaughtered, and some have even seen the ghostly re-enactment of that horrific, and very bloody battle.

Billy says: No word that has ever been uttered, no event that has ever taken place, can ever be lost. The very atmosphere that surrounds us holds on to every whisper, every thought and every action that we make, and all of these combined, are used to remind us of who we once were.

11

Ghosts of World War Two

CLINT ROAD SCHOOL (DURNING ROAD)

In November 1940, a landmine hit Clint Road Junior School, off Durning Road, killing 166 children. They had been sheltering from the air raid in the basement of the school, and the direct hit caused the boilers to explode. It was one of the saddest disasters in Liverpool at the time, and news of it spread over the entire country. The site upon which the school had stood had been left untouched until the early 1960s, when it was decided to build a new school. Before the work could begin the whole area had to be excavated, and the remains of those who had died there during the Blitz ceremoniously removed. The meticulous search for bodies was conducted undercover, and continued for several days. The new school stood in its place for some years, until that too stood empty and fell into disrepair until it was demolished. Although new houses now stand on the site, over the years passers-by have claimed that they have heard the thundering sound of an explosion, and the distant, ghostly screams of children echoing on the afternoon breeze. Even those who are not old enough to recall the sad incident could not fail to feel the heavy emotion encapsulated in the entire area of Clint Road, perhaps a constant reminder of the sadness of that fateful day in November in 1940.

THE GHOST OF FREDA

Freda was a well-known eccentric figure in Wavertree during the 1940s and 1950s. She was a very refined, German lady in her early seventies, who was frequently seen wandering the streets late at night. She lived in Wavertree Vale and, apart from the fact that she was extremely elegant, and was believed to be the daughter of a German Baron, very little was known about Freda. The shoulders of her graceful six feet tall figure were always draped with a fur stole, and she was never seen without a large brimmed hat, complete with long, multicoloured feather plume, that made the eccentric Freda even more intriguing. During the blackouts of the Second World War, Freda frequently ignored the warden's warnings about showing a light, and was eventually arrested for shining a torch into the sky while the air raid was actually in progress. Because she was quite open about why she had persistently committed the offence, the residents of Wavertree accosted her every time she was seen on the street. This did not deter Freda, who brazenly walked to the shops in nearby Lawrence Road, with her head proudly held high. Sadly, Freda died some time towards the end of the 1950s, but her ghostly figure has been seen many times in the dead of night, walking through the streets of Wavertree. Although the old terraced houses that once stood in Wavertree Vale have now been replaced by new ones, many people have claimed to have seen a very tall lady carrying a bright light, through the streets of Wavertree in the middle of the night. When she reaches Wavertree she simply disappears into the shadows.

Billy says: Maybe Freda doesn't know the war is over! Or, perhaps where she is now the war still continues!

THE HAUNTED AIR RAID SHELTER

In the early 1950s when I grew up, signs of the Second World War were still visible all over Liverpool, and although the badly scarred city struggled bravely to recover its strength, the camaraderie and determination of the people clearly helped to maintain Liverpool's pride and dignity. Every street and house bore witness to the relentless pounding the city had sustained during the six year Blitz, and even under the dark cloud that loomed over Liverpool, the light of hope still shone brightly. Through all the depression the children of Liverpool still found magic, mischief and adventure, in every fragile structure, every bomb crater and dark corner of disused air raid shelters scattered all over the city. Lawrence Road School had two air shelters, which after the war became the 'hide-out' for Jessie James' gang or Robin Hood and his Merry Men. Sometimes the dark corners harboured monsters, ghouls and even vampires. However, one day the word was given and the air raid shelter in the far corner of the playground of Lawrence Road School was quickly abandoned. A ghostly child was frequently heard whimpering in the farthest dark corner of the shelter, and once when the caretaker shone a light inside to see who it was, he saw a little boy cowering in the corner, crying. When he went inside to retrieve the child, he just disappeared right in front of him. Although nobody knew who the little boy was, his ghostly little boy's cries were frequently heard echoing through the darkness of the air raid shelter. Even when the corporation bricked up the doorways of both shelters, primarily to prevent intruders at night, the disembodied muffled whimpering of the ghostly little boy could still be heard. Eventually, the decision was taken, and the concrete and brick shelters were finally reduced to rubble, and the cried of the ghostly little boy were never heard again! Or, were they?

12

The Crystal Ball

When Julie Watson and her husband, Joey, wandered into the old junk shop in Chatsworth Street, Toxteth, they had no idea that their purchase would cause them so much misery and distress. They both shared a mutual interest in antiques, and Joey had a particular interest in pre-war toys, and it was their respective hobbies that led the couple into Fred Wilson's emporium. As soon as Julie clapped eyes on the old and very scratched crystal speculum standing amongst other junk on the cluttered shelf in the shop, she immediately decided that she must have it. She held it carefully in her hands, peering wide-eyed into its distorted surface. 'Do you think they can really see anything in crystal balls?' she said, holding it in front of her husband.

'No, it's a load of rubbish,' he quickly dismissed, moving his eyes back to the Dinky toy he was nostalgically inspecting in his hands. 'Don't know what you want that for anyway. What will you do with it?'

'I'll find a use for it,' she grinned. 'Who knows I might even start working as a clairvoyant and call myself Madam Julie.' Her husband just shook his head impatiently and rolled his eyes heavenward. 'I'll take it!' she said, handing it to the small elderly bald man quietly watching them from behind the counter.

'That'll be five shillings,' said the man eagerly, a look of achievement all over his face. 'Sorry I haven't got any bags to put it in.'

'That's alright,' Julie answered politely. 'The car's just outside.'

Long before they had reached their home in Underley Street, off Smithdown Road, Julie had already decided that the crystal ball would make a nice ornamental feature in the cabinet she had inherited from her grandmother. She had read somewhere that a crystal ball should be regularly cleansed with a saline solution and left to dry naturally in the sunlight. This process apparently gets rid of any negative vibrations and helps to re-programme the speculum in preparation for the process of prophesying the future. Although Joey sceptically thought it was a load of old cod's wallop, Julie had always been fascinated by anything to do with the supernatural. She never really intended using the crystal ball for anything other than ornamental reasons, but she did believe in treating such divinatory tools with respect. She had always been very superstitious, just like her mother, her husband always teased. To Joey's amusement Julie cleansed the crystal ball almost ritualistically, and then placed it proudly in her Gran's cabinet along with other inherited pieces. She was amazed just how well the crystal ball had cleaned up, and even remarked to Joey that the scratches were not as apparent.

Two weeks had gone by and Julie was giving the front room a last minute clean before her husband arrived home from work. It was Friday and she had taken the kids to stay with her mother for the weekend. 'A nice peaceful weekend with just the two of us!' she sighed as she pushed the vacuum quickly across the carpet. The late afternoon sun filtered through the lace curtains throwing fragmented shards off light off the crystal ball standing in the cabinet. Julie stopped for a moment mesmerised by the eye-catching display, and as the sunlight suddenly dipped behind a cloud, a shadow obscured the crystal for a few moments, before lighting it up again. It was then she thought she could see images flashing quickly across the surface of the crystal sphere, one after another, as clear as a TV picture. Unknown faces and landscapes appeared in the crystal ball, as quickly as flicking through the pages of a picture book. Enthralled, Julie moved closer to the cabinet, and was amazed to see the grotesque face of a man peering out at her, a malevolent look in his dark deep set eyes. She quickly unlocked the cabinet, pulled back the door fully and carefully retrieved the crystal ball. She held it gently in her hands and watched the man's face at it slowly metamorphosed into the face of someone both she and her husband knew well. 'My god,' she gasped. 'Peter Rid. What the…' She stopped as the face of one of Joey's oldest friends changed again into a woman's face she did not know. The image of the woman's face suddenly crumpled, almost as though she was in great pain, and then the crystal speculum was obscured as blood appeared to splash all over its surface. It looked so real that Julie dropped the crystal ball onto the floor and watched wide-eyed as it rolled across the carpet, its momentum ceasing as it reached the edge of the settee. She stopped to retrieve it and noticed that the images were no longer visible. The well polished surface of the crystal ball just glistened in the light and the reflection of Julie's own face peered out at her. She thought no more about it, and only mentioned it to her husband when he told her that he had met Peter Rid on his way home from work. 'It was probably just a trick of light.' Her husband shook his head dismissively, and huffed in his usual sceptical way. 'You know what you're like.' However, after they had eaten their evening meal Joey told his wife that a girlfriend of Peter's had been murdered some years ago, and although the police had brought his friend in for routine questioning, his watertight alibi made it clear that he had nothing whatsoever to do with it. 'Besides,' said Joey shaking the creases from the evening newspaper, 'he couldn't harm a fly, and everyone knows that!' However, Julie had a very suspicious mind, and she knew what she had seen was very real, and most certainly not her imagination at all. What she wanted to know was 'WHY she had seen what she had?'

Over a week had passed by, and Julie's daughters, Samantha and June were watching the TV in the living, whilst she caught up on some paper work in the front room where it was quiet. She despised doing her monthly accounts, and allowed her thoughts to drift for a moment away from the laborious chore of making ends meet. Her attention was suddenly caught by a piercing light on the surface of the crystal ball in the cabinet, and as she moved closer to it she saw that same grotesque face she had seen previously, staring out and grinning at her. She felt a flash of fear as the horrible face metamorphosed into the face of their friend Peter Rid. Julie felt uncomfortable, and it was almost as though he could see her peering at him in the crystal ball. She took a step back as she saw another face transfigure across the surface of the crystal speculum. It was the face of a young black woman, a look of terror in her eyes. Again, it seemed to Julie as though the young woman could see her, and was pleading to her for help. Julie could feel her heart pounding inside her chest, and watched helplessly as the brightly lit crystal fell into darkness. Now there was only the reflection of her own face on the shiny surface of the crystal ball. She sat quietly, completely numb and confused and did not know what to think. She knew it wasn't her imagination, as Joey her husband had suggested, but she just wondered what it was all about. She couldn't do anything else but try to forget the experiences. Besides, she knew her husband would only laugh at her. However, the following evening Julie couldn't believe her eyes when she saw the headlines on the front page of the Echo, and the picture of the young black girl she had seen reflected in the crystal ball: 'Twenty-two-year-old prostitute found dead in alleyway.'

'What's the matter with you?' asked Joey, noticing the concern on his wife's face. 'You look as though you've seen a ghost!'

'I think I have,' she said quietly, allowing the newspaper to fall to her lap. 'In fact, I know I have.'

She told her husband everything she had seen, and raised the newspaper to show him the headlines. Joey knew his wife well enough to know that she had not imagined it. He was concerned about her obvious distress, and could see no alternative but to get rid of the crystal ball. 'There's obviously something not quite right about it. I did warn you not to buy it. You don't know where it's come from.'

Joey insisted that they should get rid of the crystal ball right away. He stormed into the front room and collected it from the cabinet. 'Right,' he said with an urgent tone, 'I know what I'm going to do with this.' Before Julie could say anything, her husband was driving off in his car. He'd been gone for nearly an hour, and returned with a look of achievement all over his face. 'That's the end of that.'

'What have you done with it?' she asked. 'You haven't given it to someone have you?'

Joey shook his head and grinned. 'I took it to the tip.' He sat back triumphantly in the chair. 'No one will ever see that bloody thing again, that's for sure.'

Just when the couple had thought that that was the end of the whole thing, the astounding news reached them that Peter Rid had been arrested for the murder of the prostitute. 'Are the police certain it was him?' asked Julie.

'They've apparently got a lot of evidence against him. It's a cut and dried case,' said Joey, shaking his head in disbelief. 'And it looks like they're going to charge him with three other murders. I can't believe it.'

Julie felt an icy chill pass through her whole body as she recalled the images she had seen in the crystal ball. She was glad that her husband had disposed of it once and for all.

Some weeks later they called into the junk shop in Chatsworth Street, just to see if there was anything of interest to buy. 'No bloody crystal balls or ouija boards,' Joey joked, giving his wife a warning sideways glance. 'Be warned.'

On this occasion there was a middle-aged woman sitting behind the counter, reading a magazine. When the couple walked into the shop she peered over her wire-rimmed spectacles at them and smiled. 'Looking for anything in particular?' she asked politely. 'Or have you just come to browse?'

'Just come to browse,' answered Julie, following her husband to the far side of the shop. Almost at the same time they stopped in disbelief, wide-eyed as they both saw the old crystal ball sitting on the shelf amongst other miscellaneous pieces. Joey reached out and collected the crystal sphere from the shelf. 'It couldn't be,' he exclaimed, almost breathlessly. 'I threw it in the tip.' He suddenly grinned dismissively, and then returned the crystal ball to the shelf. 'It must be another one.'

Not convinced, Julie quickly retrieved the crystal ball from its resting place and began to closely examine it. 'No!' she said in no more than a whisper. 'It's the same one, I'd know it anywhere.' She pointed to a deep scratch across the smooth surface. 'Look!' she urged her husband. 'The scratch has a little loop at the end of it. This is the same one.'

'Ridiculous!' grinned Joey, turning to walk to the other side of the shop. 'I know what I did with it.'

Listening to the couple discussing the crystal, the shopkeeper removed her spectacles and placed them carefully along side the book she was reading on top of the cluttered counter. 'Is there something wrong?' she asked, pulling herself tiredly to her feet. She made her way to where Julie was standing holding the old crystal ball.

'It's an old speculum with a lot of history.'

Julie looked at the woman's lined face and could see that she knew more about it. 'We bought one just like it from here some weeks ago,' she carefully watched the woman's face for a response. 'The elderly gentleman served us.'

A slight smile dawned across the woman's thin lips. 'I'm the only who works here,' she said. 'I have owned the shop for over 10 years, and before that my father owned it.'

Julie swung round to face her husband, and then looked at the woman again. 'Maybe you were not in that day? Maybe your father was looking after things?'

'I wish that were the case!' said the woman, a far away look in her eyes. 'Although my father was a good man, he was strange with unusual beliefs.'

'Was?' interjected Joey.

'He died some years ago now. And believe me, you are not the first to say that they had bought the crystal from him. But, believe me, it has never left its place on the shelf in all these years.

'It belonged to my father, and to his father before him. I wouldn't part with it for the world. I just keep it in the shop to remind me of him.'

13

Doggie Tails

JENNY'S GONE HOME

The Ansons all agreed that the family's new Alsatian dog should be called 'Jenny', a suitable name for an extremely friendly creature with an agreeable and very loving nature. Although Jenny had been bought as a pet for the children of the house, Sydney was quite surprised when the family's new addition seemed to attach herself to him, and followed him everywhere. In fact, the two became inseparable and went everywhere together. When Sydney Anson retired for the night, usually after midnight, Jenny would finish the last of her dinner, and then patiently await her loving master's whistle, telling her that it was time for her to join him. Although Jenny was never allowed on the bed, she did sleep on a large cushion next to the dressing table, and even had her own warm duvet. The whole family had now accepted the fact that Jenny was their father's dog, and they had all become accustomed to the familiar whistle just after midnight.

The years went by and Sydney was diagnosed with terminal cancer. Being the loving family man he was, he insisted that he should spend his last weeks at home with his family. He would frequently be found sitting on the stairs struggling for breath, his faithful companion sitting by his side. Although everyone was deeply saddened when Sydney finally lost his battle against his illness, Jenny found it very difficult to function without her loving master. She wouldn't eat and quickly went into a deep depression. The vet had warned the family that they should not expect Jenny to live any longer than a few days. Sydney's daughter, Jane nursed Jenny in front of the fire, and on the evening when she drew in her last breath, Jane heard the unmistaken sound of her father whistling from upstairs. Jane's mother also heard it, and her brother who was usually a heavy sleeper, quickly came down stairs to see if everyone else had heard it. At least now the grieving family were comforted to know that their father was all right, and that he and Jenny were now together. 'Jenny has gone home, mum,' smiled Jane to her mother. 'She's with dad again.'

NOT ALL ANGELS HAVE WINGS

John and Mary Fielding had lived in their comfortable semi-detached house in Woolton Road for over 30 years, and now that the children were all married, with families of their own, and John had retired, they were both looking forward to enjoying the fruits of their labours. Apart from Bess, their black Labrador, there were only the two of them now, and so John had long since decided that they could come and go as they pleased, and that is exactly what they had planned on doing. They had booked a two-week holiday in Spain for the end of July, and on their return John had planned to take Mary to the Lake District for a week. Their next-door neighbours were going to look after Bess while they were in Spain, and when they went to the Lake District, Bess could accompany them. Since John's heart attack two years ago, he realised just how precious life was, and he now allowed nothing whatsoever to worry him.

Bess was nine years old and well and truly one of the family. John even involved the loving canine in a humorous little routine, which he had specially created when he wanted to get round Mary after an argument, or simply cajole her into doing something she didn't want to do. For example, when Mary was going about her daily chores in the kitchen, John would pretend Bess was speaking, and would shout in a strange and sometimes gruff voice, 'Dad wants a cup of tea, mum'. In fact, John had become quite proficient at throwing his voice like a ventriloquist, making it sound just like Bess was responsible. It never failed, and Mary would always stop what she was doing to make John a cup of tea. He would also use Bess as a way of calming his wife down when she was angry with him, over one thing or another. 'Don't shout at dad,' he would say in a gruff voice. 'Don't forget he's not been too well!'

Although Mary knew that it was her husband, she would always reply to Bess, tiredly shaking her head. 'Oh, I don't know...' It worked every time and would always bring laughter to the most heated moments. 'Oh, you...' she would always say, before giving Bess a big hug. John now mimicked Bess speaking so often, that Mary sometimes forgot that it was her husband and not really Bess's voice.

It was a beautiful sunny afternoon and John was mowing the back garden while Mary prepared something for lunch. The sun was shining brightly through the kitchen window, and Mary paused for a moment to watch a blackbird perched on the apple tree in the garden. Suddenly she heard the familiar funny voice coming from the hallway behind her.

'Come quickly, mum. Dad's lying on the ground holding his chest.'

'Oh stop it!' she snapped, placing the tea towel on the edge of the draining board. 'That's not funny, John!'

She popped her head into the hallway to find Bess sitting there alone, with an anxious look in her eyes.

'John?' she called, walking into the living room to see if her husband was there. The room was empty, and Mary began to feel a little anxious. 'John, are you in the bathroom?'

She stood for a moment at the foot of the stairs, but her thoughts were once again interrupted by the funny voice, 'Quickly, dad can't breathe. He's in the garden.'

Mary suddenly swung her head round to see Bess again going through the back door into the garden. She followed her quickly and could see John lying doubled-up on the grass. His face was purple and he was obviously having difficulty breathing.

'Oh! My God!' gasped Mary, moving her husband into the recovery position and calling to her neighbour to ring for an ambulance. In no time at all, the paramedics had arrived and john was taken to hospital. After spending a few days in intensive care he was moved into a side ward.

'You're lucky to be alive!' said the doctor. 'If it hadn't been for your wife's quick thinking, you wouldn't be with us now, you know.'

Mary took hold of John's hand and squeezed it tightly.

'We have Bess to thank,' she said, smiling. 'It was her quick thinking that saved the day.'

'Who's Bess?' asked the doctor. 'Your daughter?'

'No!' smiled Mary. 'Bess is our dog. Our very special dog.'

She glanced at John and they both smiled. Mary leaned in closer to her husband. 'You'll never know how special Bess really is. I'll tell you one day.'

Billy says: Believe it or not, this is based on a very true story, and one that has been verified by more than two people. And so you see, not all angels have wings! That is a fact!

FAITHFUL BLACKIE

John Fisk and his little black mongrel, Blackie, had been inseparable right up until John's death in 1956. Blackie had been John's constant companion since his wife, Margaret, had died six years before, and before John himself died he made his daughter promise that she would look after his faithful four-legged friend. When John died after a twelve-month illness, everyone at the funeral was surprised to see that Blackie had followed the hearse to Springwood cemetery, where the funeral was to take place, a few miles from his new home in Aigburth. No attempt was made to remove the devoted little dog from the chapel, and mourners watched as Blackie lay patiently by his master's coffin for the duration of the service. For two years up until the day Blackie died, he would be seen every day lying by his master's grave, obviously fretting his life away. After the loyal little dog died, they say of a broken heart, his ghostly form was still frequently seen lying by the grave.

Billy says: Such a demonstration of loyalty is quite common, and was also seen in the famous story of Greyfriar's Bobby, where a small dog in Edinburgh remained by its master's grave until the day he himself died. I was told this story by John Fisk's niece.

14

Humorous Side of a Séance

Veteran medium, Eddie Emmery (now deceased) was perhaps one of the last of a dying breed of mediums and, in my opinion, one of the best exponents of mental mediumship in the 20th century. Eddie had sat in a closed physical circle for many years, and really looked forward to the Friday night meeting with other like-minded people. Although now in his early eighties, the supervising medium had run the circle for over 15 years, and had earned the respect of everyone who knew him. At least seven of the 11 people in the circle were already working mediums, and attended the Friday circle primarily to support the elderly medium and experience the different phenomena that took place each week. This would be anything from disembodied voices resounding through the aluminium trumpet, to apports dropping onto the sitter's laps. Eddie Emmery suddenly became suspicious of the consistency of the phenomena and began to wonder how it could be guaranteed and be so consistent. As the séance always began at 8pm prompt, the 11 sitters would mostly arrive at the Victorian Terrace in Bowring Park, just after 7.30pm.

This gave everyone time to relax before entering the séance room at the top of the house, the door of which was always kept locked throughout the week, and was usually only opened by the medium's wife at 7.40pm on the night of the séance. The routine was the same every Friday, and everyone had become accustomed to it.

Each week everyone would leave the séance with an apport, which would be a small artefact, such as a lucky charm, a ring or some other small item, that appeared seemingly from nowhere, and dropped onto the sitter's lap. An aluminium trumpet was also used to amplify disembodied voices that would speak to selected members of the séance. Eddie's suspicions prompted him to investigate the séance room before the other sitters took up their respective places. Excusing himself, he made his way up to the bathroom, across the landing from the séance room, and snuck quietly in to look around. Eddie had always held the elderly medium in high esteem, and was shocked to find a secret draw under his seat, full of tiny artefacts, which would later be used as apports during the séance. After removing the objects from the secret draw, he mischievously replaced them with the bag of Jelly Babies he loved and always carried with him.

The séance began at 8pm prompt, and after the usual philosophical talk by the medium's spirit guide, the apports began to fall through the darkness onto each sitters lap. 'Jelly Babies!' They all mumbled in unison. 'I love these!' giggled Eddie, pushing his Jelly Baby cheekily into his mouth. 'I'll have yours if you don't want them!'

It was later discovered that because the elderly medium's abilities had waned, he had also been manually moving the aluminium trumpet around the circle, and had been feigning all the phenomena for years. Needless to say, as a result of Eddie's suspicions, the circle disbanded and the medium retired.

GABRIEL'S TRUMPET

The very fact that the Victorian Séance had to be conducted in a perfectly blacked out room, was frequently too much of a temptation for the dishonest medium. Although the majority of those who conducted the 'parlour séance' were quite honest, there was a minority (even today) who were anything but genuine. Ron Ferguson had devoted his life to his mid-week séance, with the sole intention of witnessing even more extraordinary phenomena. Although he had no real desire himself to be a medium, he did believe in Jack Platt, the circle's supervising medium. Each week the aluminium trumpet would be ceremoniously placed on the highly polished table in the centre of the circle, and when the medium was satisfied that the conditions were exactly right, the lights would be extinguished and the prayer would be said. There were four women and four men in the circle, and these had regularly attended for the past four and half years. It was always the same routine each week; First to stand up would be Ron expounding his personal philosophical views, and then the trumpet would rise about eighteen inches into the air, move around the circle at an incredible speed, before stopping at a selected member of the group. Anonymous disembodied voices would speak, before the trumpet returned to its resting place on the table. It was always an enjoyable experience, and the evening was always concluded with a hymn and then a closing prayer. To ensure total darkness, specially adapted black shutters had been fitted to the windows in the séance room. In fact, it was so dark in the room, you could not see the person sitting next to you. This week Ron stood up and gave his usual philosophical talk. He was feeling particularly inspired this night, and so it was a little longer than usual. As always, on the conclusion of Ron's address, he paused for a moment and drew in a deep breath, and when he stepped back to sit down, he stumbled heavily over something, fell back and cracked his head on a large cabinet behind his chair. Ron lost consciousness for a few moments, and in the panic the lights were turned on. Everyone was amazed to see the supervising medium on his hands and knees in the centre of the circle, holding the aluminium trumpet to his lips. 'I was just making certain it was in the correct position!' he explained, a guilty expression across his face. The medium had obviously been faking the paranormal phenomena all these years; and the disembodied voices that had enthralled everyone for so long, had all been produced by the medium himself. Ron's only concern was finding his false teeth. They had fallen out in the commotion and had found their way to the top of the medium's head.

15

The Ghost of Blackstone Street

The railway bridge in Blackstone Street is said to have been the scene of a horrific Victorian murder, and many people have said that they have witnessed a 'replay' of the grisly event whilst walking through the railway arch at night. On Sunday evening, sometime around 10pm, in January 1884, a Spanish Merchant Seaman was returning to his ship in Huskinsson Dock,

when he was set upon by a gang of youths. Although initially the young sailor escaped, the gang pursued him and eventually caught him under the railway arch in Blackstone Street. Although it is said that the young man pleaded for his assailants to leave him alone, they just laughed and continued to kick and beat him, concluding their horrific attack by stabbing him to death. It is said that the ground where the young seafarer lay was awash with blood, and the perpetrators of the crime spat on the body and cheered triumphantly about what they I had done.

Although many years have now gone by since that dismal night, it is said that the young sailor's cries are sometimes heard, particularly when the wind is blowing softly from the Mersey. Many people have seen ghostly images around the spot where he is said to have died, and others have witnessed unusual light anomalies moving across the surface of the ground.

Billy says: This is just another example to show that nothing is ever forgotten, and that the environmental memory compartmentalises every event and every minute detail, even when the shadows of time conceal the truth, the very air that we breath recalls everything that has passed us by.

16

The Cursed House

Garmoyle Road runs from Gainsbourgh Road right along to Smithdown Road, and although today most of the terraced houses are flats, in the 1940s and 1950s the houses in Garmoyle Road were occupied by professional people and were regarded as desirable residences and very much sought-after. However, a very dark cloud looms heavily over one particular house, not too far from Gainsbourgh Road. (The number can't be given for obvious reasons.) It was there, some time in the 1940s, that a woman suffering from depression hanged herself in the hallway. Devastated by her death, the husband decided to move out with his children, and the house lay empty for two years. Unaware of its past, the following couple to occupy the house had only lived there for 18 months before the previous horrific scenario repeated itself. Devastated with his unexpected redundancy, the middle-aged father of three took his own life by taking an overdose of sleeping pills. Once again the dark cloud of misfortune loomed heavily over the house, and stood empty for a further two years. The third family to live there did so quietly happily until the mid 1950s. The next person to move in to the house was a woman and her 18-year-old son. Unable to cope with her recent divorce, she took her own life, and exactly 12 months later, to the very day, her son was tragically killed on his motorbike. After a fire, the house with the extremely dismal past was empty for many years, but today has been turned into flats.

Billy says: Although I have known about the house since I was a young boy, a relative of one of the misfortunate families related the details of the unhappy events to me. I am quite certain we can dismiss the possibility of coincidence in this case, and as none of the families involved had known about had happened there previously, we must consider the possibility of a 'malevolent abode'. Houses, like people, can be born out of evil!

17

The Mystery of Polly Bradshaw

When casually strolling down Rodney Street at night, it doesn't take much imagination to be transported back through time to when horse-drawn cabbies made their way down the cobbled street, and bonneted ladies and men with top hats and frock coats could be seen, wending their way home beneath the flickering lights of Victorian Liverpool. The whole ambience of Rodney Street is the culmination of many historical events, many of which are best forgotten. However, it would seem that the infamous James William Mackenzie is the only notorious figure ever remembered when speaking about Rodney Street's paranormal history. Rodney Street is the home to many other ghostly characters, now long since lost in time.

After the death of her mother in 1890, slightly built 20-year-old Polly Bradshaw moved from Widnes to Liverpool to live with her mother's only sister, Mary. Mary lived alone in Carter Street, Toxteth, and the last thing that Polly had promised her mother before she died, was that she would look after Mary. Polly had always been an unusual girl, and had apparently inherited her mother's 'special' gift of prophesying the future and speaking with the so-called 'dead'. She took a job as pantry maid for the Martin family at 55 Rodney Street, and although the lady of the house wanted Polly to live in, she explained that she needed to look after her sick aunt in Carter Street. Not wanting to lose the hard-working girl, Martha Martin agreed. Although it's not quite clear

how exactly, Polly Bradshaw soon became known for her unusual skills as a seer and medium, and would frequently be invited to the homes of merchants living in Rodney Street, to conduct the very popular Victorian pastime of the 'Parlour séance'. The young

Polly became very popular and was invited to the homes of some of the wealthiest people in the area. However, knowledge of her unusual skills was brought to the attention of the local church, the priest of which made some very strong protestations to the constabulary, demanding her immediate arrest. Seeing no real harm in what young Polly was doing, the attending police sergeant just gave her a stern warning, and told her such practises were illegal. No further action was taken, until it was discovered that she had ignored the warning and continued to conduct séances and other 'unusual' behaviour. A local magistrate who lived in Rodney Street, and who was known to regularly attend one of Polly's séances, discreetly had a word with her. It is said that she became so well known, that she did not seem at all surprised when a well-dressed gentleman from London called to see her on a matter of great urgency. As requested, Polly entered the drawing where her mistress and the mysterious gentlemen were waiting for her. It is said that he carried an invitation from Queen Victoria, who desperately wanted to see the young medium privately. With the permission of her mistress, Polly left for London, but never returned to Liverpool. In fact, Polly was never seen again. When friends of hers called to her aunt Mary's home in Carter Street to find out what had happened to her, someone else occupied her house.

Billy says: My aunt Louise, who was also a medium, gave this story to me. It is a known fact that Queen Victoria consulted many mediums during her lifetime, in an attempt to make contact with Albert, her dead husband, who died in 1861. It is believed that Queen Victoria mourned Albert right up until the day she died on January 22, 1901. Her faithful companion, John Brown (a distant relation of my wife's mother) was also believed to be a medium, and his communications with the Queen's 'dead' husband helped her through her grieving period.

18

The Mystery of the Cat Woman of Toxteth

Very little was actually known about Marie Greer except that she had appeared on the stages of music halls all over Britain. Although she was now in her late eighties, she had obviously been a beautiful woman in her day and even now would not be seen in public without looking immaculate. Marie lived alone with her two cats in one of the big Victorian houses in Upper Parliament Street, where she had lived since she was a young girl. Although she was extremely eccentric in both her habits and the way she lived, she was still mentally alert and just as physically mobile as she was when she was 50.

She had never married, this much everyone knew. However, there had been many suitors in her younger days and it was known that she had once been engaged to be married. Her fiancé, however, had been killed in the First World War, and Marie had vowed that nobody would ever take his place.

Marie carried her love of animals to the extreme and could be seen after midnight each night, walking the streets of Toxteth carrying a large basket crammed with cat and dog food. Her route was always carefully planned, and although her time often varied each night, her canine and feline orphans were still there in their groups, waiting patiently to be fed.

By day, Marie could be seen going through the same procedure with the pigeons around Granby Street and Kingsley Road and, regardless of what time she came to feed them, they seemed to always know when she was coming and would flock there in their hundreds.

Marie always made a special effort in the winter months and would make two, and sometimes three, feeding visits a day. It was late December 1957 and it looked like it might snow. There was an extremely cold chill in the air and yet the day was bright and clear. On her way to feed the pigeons in Kingsley Road, Marie always popped in to the local newsagents to say hello to the proprietor, Dolly McNally, and to purchase two ounces of Imperial Creams, her only vice. Thursday was usually a particularly busy day for Marie, as she ended her day with a trip to the Pier Head to feed the seagulls. Dolly was a little concerned as she hadn't been in to see her. She had known Marie for a long time and was only too aware that there must be something wrong if she had not called in to her shop.

So, as soon as she had closed for the day, she went round to Marie's house. Dolly was forever telling her to sell up and move to something smaller and more manageable. The house was far too big for one person and only part of it was occupied anyway. But Marie had lived there most of her life and simply refused to leave.

'They'll carry me out in a box!' she had always said to Dolly. 'This is my home and this is where I'll stay!'

Dolly got no reply at Marie's home and noticed that the curtains in the front room were still drawn. She felt there must be something wrong and she quickly returned home and telephoned the police.

The two policemen who called at the house tried knocking and ringing the bell for 20 minutes but failed to get any response. The door was eventually broken open and they were instantly overwhelmed by the pungent smell of cats and dogs. They discovered Marie Greer's body in bed, but were prevented from getting near her by over 30 cats and as many dogs, standing in vigil over her body. Pigeons, too, flew freely around the bedroom and seemed to be trying to prevent any effort by anyone to get near Marie's lifeless body.

The 'cat woman', as she had affectionately been known, had died naturally in her sleep. Nobody had any idea of how the old woman had been living. It baffled the police how she managed to get so many cats, dogs and pigeons into her home, and it still remains a mystery to this very day.

Billy says: My parents had known the so-called 'cat woman' for many years. Because some of her family are still alive, I have changed her name to avoid any distress.

19

Ghostly Hospital Tales

One would expect all hospitals to have ghosts of one kind or another, considering how many people have died in them. Over the years I have collected a lot of eerie tales about ghostly nurses, and disembodied voices echoing down hospital corridors.

A porter working at The Royal Liverpool Hospital related the following spooky tales to me.

Craig McManus had worked at the hospital as a porter for three years and had experienced many strange happenings during that time. Most of his experiences took place in the dead of night, when there was no one else around, and so could be put down to either an overactive imagination, or as straightforward coincidence. However, what happened to him on November 21, 1987 was most definitely not a figment of his imagination. He was on a late shift and was not due to finish work until 7am the following morning. Greg did not mind doing the late shift as there was always something to keep him occupied, ensuring that he never got bored. He had been asked to collect some pillows from a ward on the third floor and, on top of all the other jobs he had to do, he was beginning to feel the pressure. He was way behind with his chores and was rushing as fast as he could to try and catch up with his busier than normal schedule.

The lift doors opened with their usual clang and he stepped in. The lift began to rise again but stopped suddenly at the second floor level. The doors opened and an unaccompanied girl, aged about 12, entered. Greg was so preoccupied, with all the jobs he had to do, that he never stopped to think what someone so young was doing walking around the hospital, so late at night, on her own.

The lift stopped at the third floor and Greg stepped out into the corridor. He suddenly realised that the little girl was still in the lift behind him and he glanced back to see if she had followed him into the corridor. But the lift was empty and there was no sign of her anywhere.

He told another porter about the experience and he too had encountered the same, unaccompanied little girl in the early hours of one November night. Further enquiries revealed that the ghostly apparition had been seen on numerous occasions over the past 20 years and all the descriptions of her corresponded with each other. Even today, she is occasionally still seen and yet nobody seems to know who she is, or where she is going.

THE GHOSTLY VISITOR

Although these days hospital visiting times are fairly flexible, until about 20 years ago, they were very strict and limited to one hour per patient, per day, and a restriction of two visitors per bed at any one time.

Sister Jan Jenkins was extremely conscientious and would always call the visitors to time, dead on the hour. After supper she would make her routine inspection of the ward and when she was quite satisfied that everything was quite in order, lights were out at 9pm prompt. She gave a whole new meaning to the word efficiency and, although she was an extremely hard taskmaster, she was greatly respected by all her staff.

It had been a busy week and Sister Jenkins was feeling quite stressed. Her staff knew what she was like when she was in one of her moods, so everything was done to keep in her good books or, at least, stay out of her way.

When all the visitors had gone and the patients were being settled down for the night, Sister Jenkins marched sternly through the ward and side rooms in typical, sergeant major fashion, checking that all the visitors had gone and that there were no patients slyly sneaking a last cigarette.

As she entered the day room, she noticed that there was a woman, obviously not a patient because she was fully clothed, sitting in the chair in front of the TV set, smoking a cigarette. Not only had the visitor broken the rules by remaining after visiting time, but had also left the TV on. Sister Jenkins was outraged and marched boldly past her towards the television.

'Visiting time finished 15 minutes ago!' she said sharply, turning the TV off and spinning round to face the woman.

Her eyes widened in disbelief, however, as an empty chair confronted her, in fact, an empty room. The woman had disappeared completely, without even leaving the smell of cigarette smoke behind her. She hurried into the corridor but still there was no sign of the woman anywhere. Sister Jenkins could feel goosebumps erupting all over her body and felt as though someone had just walked over her grave.

'The woman was sitting there in front of the TV,' she assured herself, 'and as she was quite elderly, she couldn't possibly have left the room so quickly. Anyway, I don't believe in ghosts! There must be a rational explanation, but what?'

Sister Jenkins was never able to come up with one!

THE HARBINGER OF DEATH

The next story also happened on the same ward and involved two porters who wish to remain anonymous so their names have been changed for the purpose of the story.

Ron Edwards and Phil Platt were transporting a middle-aged gentleman from the medical assessment room to a ward capable of treating his illness. Although the man had been brought to hospital as an urgent case, his condition was now stable. As they pushed the trolley from the lift into the corridor, a stern faced young woman, dressed all in black, passed them to enter the lift. As she did so, she whispered something to Ron Edwards.

'He won't make it to the ward!'

Before he could say anything to her, the lift doors had closed and the woman had completely vanished!

'She's off her head!' he said to Phil in a quiet voice. 'Did you hear that?'

'No!' Phil replied, shaking his head. 'The look of her was quite enough. She looked like something out of a horror movie.'

However, by the time they had reached the ward, to their horror, the patient they were transferring had died of a massive heart attack.

It is said that the spooky woman, dressed all in black, has been seen many times in different hospitals over the years, whispering the same prophetic message into the ear of an unsuspecting porter, as he transports his patient to his, or her, final destination.

GHOSTLY FACES

Seeing so-called 'dead' people was commonplace to me as a child, and very rarely did a day go by when I did not experience something of a paranormal nature. Because of an incurable respiratory disease I contracted when I was a baby, I spent most of my life in and out of hospital. When I was two years old I was admitted to Woolton Baby Hospital (no longer there) where I remained for over 12 months. In those days they believed in as much fresh air as possible to aid recovery, and so every morning my cot would be pushed on to an open veranda where it would remain until the sun went down. One occasion, which I remember clearly, my mother took some photographs of me standing on the veranda wall. When they were developed ghostly faces could be seen on one of them. I do believe that the face above my head, on the glass roof, is the face of Tall Pine, a Spirit Guide with whom I have been acquainted since I was a child. His face frequently appeared on photographs when I was a young boy. When my autobiography was published in 1995, the publishers, Harper Collins, had the photograph tested to see if the ghostly phenomenon was the result of light or even dust on the lens. Kodak affirmed that there was no reason for the 'extra image', and they also stated that they had no idea what caused it.

Billy says: I have included the photograph so that you can see for yourself. Because of the way it has been reproduced in the book you may have some difficulty at first actually seeing the face. It can be seen at the top, almost in the centre of the photograph, on the glass-panelled roof. The light anomalies seen streaming through the photograph could not be explained either. A sketch of Tall Pine can be seen elsewhere in the book.

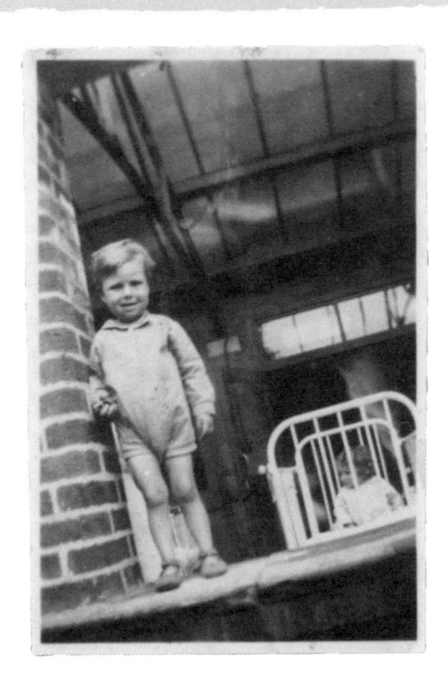

20

Dead Man's Handwriting

Although quite rare, 'Automatic Writing' was a common and very popular phenomenon during Victorian times, and was often demonstrated for the amusement of those who attended the 'parlour' séance. This phenomenon involves the writer's pen moving involuntarily across the surface of the paper, and the writing that is produced is completely different to the person's own handwriting. The most famous of all automatists was Geraldine Cummings, who wrote many books through the process of automatic writing, claiming that these were from the pen of deceased authors.

The following two examples of automatic writing are true stories, and although neither story is in anyway connected to the other, I personally knew both people involved.

Dora Birkhead was a retired headmistress and had been widowed for two years. Although the couple had made a lot of plans for their retirement, fate had played a cruel part in their lives, and now she was forced to face life without her devoted husband of 35 years. She spent most of her spare time these days writing poetry, and as she was quite gifted with words, had decided to have a go at writing a novel. It was around 3pm one sunny spring afternoon, and Dora was sitting writing at her desk under the window at the front of her semi-detached house. She looked out onto the garden and remarked to herself just how beautiful everything looked this time of the year, when some movement caught her attention across the road. She noticed a funereal cortège pulling up outside number 48, and remembered that Jean's husband had died suddenly, causing memories of her own husband's funeral to come flooding back into her mind. She empathised with Jean and knew exactly how she would be feeling at that moment, and what she would be going through. Primarily as a mark of respect she watched until the final car had pulled away from the door, at which point she lowered her eyes to the paper lying on the desk in front of her. She was surprised to see that without realising it she had scribbled on several pieces of the paper, and although the writing was illegible scrawl, she could see at first glance that it was definitely not her own neat, and very readable script. On closer inspection she could just about make out some sort of letter that began 'My darling Jean…' and was signed at the end 'Your loving husband Ron'. Not knowing what to make of the writing, Dora sat back in the chair and read it from beginning to end. 'My darling Jean,' it began, 'I'm so sorry that I had to leave you at this time in our lives, but I just want you to know that I love you so much, and I would not have got through the last six months had it not been for you. You did all that you could to make my last months comfortable and happy, and I just wait until that day when we can be together again. Your loving husband Ron.'

Dora was overcome with emotion, and swallowed hard as a tear found its way to her cheek. She didn't have a clue what had happened, until she turned to the next page. 'Dear Dora, Please give this letter to Jean. She will be able to see that it is my writing, and she will understand exactly why I have contacted you in this way. Tell her I am alright. Best wishes Ron.'

Dora then realised that Jean's dead husband had contacted her in some way, and for a moment selfishly wondered why her own husband, Jim, had not thought of doing the same. She mulled over it for a couple of days, unable to decide what to do. The last thing she wanted was to upset Jean even further, or for Jean to fall out with her. But after reading Ron's letter again, she decided to take it over to her neighbour, who was tidying the rose bushes in the front garden.

To Dora's surprise, Jean immediately identified her dead husband's writing, and held the letter close to her chest. 'Thank you so much!' she said, dabbing her eyes with a tissue. 'This is my husband's writing. Before Ron died he told me he would send me a message in the most unlikely way. You were in the garden at the time, and he pointed to you and joked: 'I'll tell Dora I'm alright.'

At that moment Dora Birkhead was overwhelmed with a huge warmth and sense of peace. She reached over and kissed her neighbour on the cheek, before turning to make her way back across the street. She wasn't sure exactly what had happened, but she did have a strong feeling that this was just the beginning of an unusual journey.

Billy says: Dora Birkhead was right, and this was the beginning for her as an autonomist. She went on to receive writings from her own dead husband, and was also consulted by hundreds of people from all over the country. She never did write her novel, but at least she did find peace and fulfilment.

LETTERS FROM ANOTHER WORLD

Bill and Flo Chadwick were both retired and had recently moved to a nice semi-detached house in Huyton. Although it needed a few things doing to it, Bill had been a joiner by profession, and was used to turning his hand to almost anything. Flo had already decided how she wanted the kitchen to look, and had told Bill that she wanted fitted wardrobes, Bill's speciality. The couple had been married for nearly 40 years, and although they had not been blessed with children, they did have a five-year-old Alsatian dog, they called 'Cooper'. It took them a good six months to get the house more or less how they wanted it, and were planning to go to their caravan in Rhyl for a week at the end of June. Flo was cooking the evening meal, and Bill was measuring up for a shed at the end of the garden. 'Don't be too long!' Flo warned him. 'Twenty minutes and the meal will be ready.' Billy knew only too well that his wife did not like to be disobeyed, and just nodded, raising his eyes heavenward as he went into the garden holding a note pad and pen.

Already 40 minutes had gone by, and Flo had begun to distribute the potatoes and carrots and wanted Bill to carve the meat, as he always did. She had called him several times to no avail, and so decided to walk to the bottom of the garden to give him a piece of her mind. She found her husband standing by the bushes at the far end by the fence, staring into space and mumbling to himself. His face was ashen and his eyes were wide and distant. He seemed to be completely oblivious to her presence, and ignored her when she spoke. 'Bill, are you ok?' she said, concerned, waving her hand in front of his face. 'The meal's on the table. Come on, love, I want you to calve the joint.' After a while he seemed to collect his thoughts and followed his wife back down the garden towards the house. After they had eaten Bill showed his wife the note pad. It was full of strange writing, pages upon pages of illegible scrawl, with no breaks between the words, and each sentence running into the other. 'Look!' he said, excitedly. 'Read this.' Although Flo's eyesight was not good, she could see that her husband was determined for her to read what was written on the pad, and so she did her best. She knew her husband's handwriting, and knew only too well that the scrawl on the paper was not his. He had a meticulous hand, and always took care when writing. This annoyed Flo at times, as her own handwriting was very untidy and so illegible that nobody except Bill could read it. 'What is it?' she asked, glancing at her husband with some concern. 'Who wrote that?'

'It's our John's writing!' he explained. 'There's a lot more there.' He poked the writing pad sharply with his finger. 'It just kept coming.'

'Your John's dead!' Flo snapped dismissively. 'When did he write that?'

Bill stood up, angrily snatching the writing pad from her hands. 'He wrote it before. He used my hand!' Flo was suddenly overcome with concern. She knew her husband so well, and he never lost his temper under any circumstances.

'I don't understand what you mean, Bill?'

'My hand just moved of its own accord, and this is what was on the paper.'

'But Bill...' Flo stuttered. 'John's been dead for over 15 years. How could he write anything?'

Bill stormed from the room and went back into the garden where he remained for another two hours. Over the days that followed Flo grew more and more concerned about her husband. He had become irrational and extremely unpredictable, and would stay up until the early hours of the morning producing page after page of the strange writing. After comparing the writing produced by her husband, with some writing in an old ledger of Bill's brother, Flo did have to admit that there was a remarkable likeness. She was just concerned for her husband's psychological health and didn't know who to turn to. At her wit's end Flo was given my phone number. Although I could see that Bill was obviously receiving communication from his 'dead' brother, John through the process of automatic writing, it was also quite obvious to me that he was suffering some sort of psychological breakdown. The more I tried to deter him from the unhealthy practice, the angrier he became. I knew then that I couldn't help him and that he needed professional medical help.

Flo kept in touch with me, and Bill continued to receive communication from his dead brother, his mother and father and a deceased childhood friend. Then, one day, the content of the writing changed dramatically, becoming extremely abusive with foul language interjected all through the text. All this proved far too much for Bill and he finally had a nervous breakdown and had to be hospitalised. Thankfully, he made a full recovery, and today lives a quiet, and very happy life with his wife Flo, and their

Alsatian Cooper.

Billy says: I had known Bill and Flo for some years, and although he no longer allowed the so-called 'automatic writing' to control his life, against his wife's better judgement, he still occasionally did it, but only when his wife and medium friend supervised it.

21

Parklea Manor Revisited

As far as I am concerned Parklea Manor is most probably one of the most haunted houses in Liverpool, and a location that has, until now, escaped the fashionable investigations of parapsychologists and ghost hunting teams. In my previous book I wrote about some of the spooky goings on at the old house, but as the phenomena is so very varied and interesting, I think it is worthy of another mention here.

Although now in a very sorry and dilapidated state, Parklea Manor, 6 Fulwood Park, Aigburth, stands as a reminder of the opulence once enjoyed by the wealthy merchants of Liverpool in the 19th century. Although now long since gone, large ornate gates once made the leafy suburban road secure within its own private community, in itself a symbol of wealth and success. As I have previously said, Parklea Manor was once the home of Margaret Blackler, the heir to the Blackler fortune, and owner of the well-known department store, once situated on the corner of Elliot Street and Great Charlotte Street in Liverpool city centre.

As well as the ghostly figures that constantly roam through corridors and rooms of Parklea Manor, a disembodied withered hand strokes the hair of anyone who dares to enter the panelled room in the West Wing. Nobody escapes the withered hand's gentle caress, nor is the sceptic exempt from its icy touch. Now in the hands of property developers with plans to transform the old house into luxury apartments, the dead have been disturbed, and

Parklea Manor's cries can constantly be heard in the dead of night. After feeling the withered hand running through his hair, one of the property developers made a hasty retreat from the house, and refused to return.

A man in Victorian clothes is frequently seen walking down the stairs and through a wall where a door used to be. His footsteps echo through the house, and occasionally he is heard laughing mockingly, perhaps daring those who see him to follow. The ghostly apparition is even seen in the middle of the day, and although he appears to follow the same route down the stairs each time, witnesses have said that he never seems to wear the same clothes twice.

Although the old house was built in 1840, allegedly after the abolition of slavery in Great Britain, the tunnels beneath the house bear witness to the grisly trade that today torments the very conscience of humanity. Although now bricked up to prevent rats from entering from the nearby River Mersey, it is believed that slaves were kept in the cellars whilst awaiting transportation to other countries. Disembodied cries, thought to be the sound of distressed slaves, are frequently heard echoing through the dark tunnels beneath the house. A demonic disembodied head with fiendish bulging red eyes has been seen by many people, floating menacingly through the darkness in the tunnels beneath the old house.

Whilst descending the stone steps into the basement, the previous owner was confronted by a lady wearing a long white pinafore dress and bonnet, grinning insanely, before disappearing into thin air.

A ghostly choir has also been heard singing carols on Christmas Eve in the library, and the sounds of a string quartet is frequently heard resounding through the house in the middle of the night. The chatter of female voices is frequently heard coming down the stairs, and the smell of cigars sometimes clings to the air in the study.

There is very little doubt that Parklea Manor has borne silent witness to many joyous and horrific scenes, and now faced with its own demise, is perhaps giving up all its ghosts.

22

The Mystery of Teresa Helena Higginson

Few people will perhaps know the name of Teresa Helena Higginson, a 19th century prophet, seer and marked with the wounds of the Crucifixion. This diminutive, and very humble lady, was born in 1844, and was destined for a life of hardship and pain. In 1854, at the age of 10, she was sent with her sisters to be educated in the Convent of Mercy in Nottingham, where she stayed until she was 21. She then went to live in St Helens with her family, where they remained for a while until her father's business got into some financial difficulties, and he was made bankrupt. Circumstances then forced the Higginson family to move to Liverpool, where Teresa used her sewing skills to make extra money to make ends meet. The family then moved to Egremont, Wirral, but here Teresa was too ill to work and remained at home, where her sisters nursed her back to health. She eventually got a job as a teacher, and very quickly won the respect of everyone. Teresa was extremely religious and was known to devote two hours each day to prayer, and began to have prophetic visions. She confided in Father Powell, a catholic priest, about her visions, and although initially he was concerned for her psychological health, he became convinced that they were genuine. She also told her friend, fellow teacher, Susan Ryland that Our Lady occasionally appeared to her, and as a mark of discipline and respect for the Holy visitation, she would fast regularly. She and Susan Ryland took rooms together, and her friend frequently witnessed Teresa in a trance-like state, with blood oozing from wounds in her hands and feet. Father Powell was her spiritual adviser and confidant, and witnessed the frail Teresa in states of 'ecstasy' and speaking in a voice that was not her own. Sometimes telekinetic phenomena would occur whilst she was asleep, and a disembodied hand would appear to be trying to pull her from the bed. She would frequently be heard screaming mercifully as though in pain, and an invisible force would appear to be throwing everything about the bedroom. She once explained to the priest that 'The devil comes for me!' and he would make every attempt to 'exorcise the demon' to no avail. Some of her friends would be amazed when small artefacts would appear seemingly from nowhere in front of Teresa, and she would sit for hours writing long letters in handwriting that was not her own. She prophesied future wars, in which 'huge flying machines would attack Britain, and long ships would sail beneath the waters of the seas.' She even prophesied the building of the of the city's Catholic Cathedral.

In 1900, Teresa went on a pilgrimage with a friend to Rome, and even had an audience with Pope Pius X. The diminutive Teresa is believed to have had a profound effect on the Pope, who could see she was quite special.

Teresa Helena Higginson's prophesies were well documented, and her friend and spiritual confidant, Father Powell, kept all her letters. Teresa taught in schools all over the UK, and in 1905, whilst preparing to return to her family home in Neston for Christmas, she had a stroke and died. Her sisters brought her body back to Neston and buried her in her mother's grave. Although Teresa Helena Higginson's name is not on the grave, today it is a place of pilgrimage. Her friend, Father Powell, once said of her that 'Teresa is essentially a contemplative saint rather than an active one. Regardless of his statement, Teresa Helena Higginson is believed to be a modern-day saint, and steps have been taken to beatify her.

Billy says: Since writing the story of Teresa Helena Higginson, I have located the exact whereabouts of her grave. It is not in Neston as every writer on the Internet reports, but in Little Neston. Her grave can be found in the small and yet very peaceful graveyard of St Winefride's Church, and is marked by a four feet stone cross. Although when she was originally laid to rest her name was not on the gravestone, since then a plaque with her name inscribed on it has been placed on the grave. The cross is adorned with religious artefacts, such as Rosary Beads and cards, and an abundance of flowers, proof that she is most certainly held in very high esteem. As my wife and I were photographing the grave, we saw Teresa Helena's face transfigured on a tiny portion of the worn cross. As we stood, amazed we then noticed the diminutive figure of a lady standing between the gravestones, a few yards away. The woman was dressed in a long black dress and had a dark woollen shawl pulled tightly over her head. We naturally thought she was tending a grave, but when we looked back at her she had gone.

23

Dead Man's Money

As well as being very popular on the Spiritualist circuit, Dorothy and Rob Dane also ran a second hand furniture shop on Prescot Road, and had done so for the past 30 years. Although Rob wasn't a medium as such, he used to accompany his wife on the rostrum whilst she gave her well-received demonstration of clairvoyance. Dorothy was an excellent medium, and everyone used to be enthralled by Rob's oratory skills, which never failed to hold the attention of the congregation wherever they appeared. Although in their late seventies, all week the couple kept themselves very busy buying and selling furniture from their small shop. As Dorothy was the business minded one of the couple, every Thursday without fail, she would go to Hartley's Auction Room in nearby Moss Street, where she would purchase more furniture with which to stock up the shop. She had gone through the same routine for 30 years, and had become quite well known to everyone who frequented the auctions. Rob knew his wife well enough and always trusted her judgement about the items she bought, and on her return knew better than to question her about the items she had purchased. Rob had been a French Polisher by trade, and so whenever any of the furniture looked a little worse for wear, he would sand the item down to the bear wood, apply a couple of coats of stain, and restore the piece to its former glory. In fact, apart from being happily married, the couple had an extremely good working relationship.

Friday morning as usual, the van pulled up outside the shop, and the furniture Dorothy had bought at the auction the day before was unloaded.

Rob surveyed the shop full of furniture, remarking to himself that his wife's judgement was always right. His eyes suddenly fell on a beautiful Victorian Mahogany chest of draws, and apart from a few surface marks, it was almost pristine. When the shop had closed at 5.30pm on the dot, Rob decided to immediately get to work on this nice piece of furniture. He had removed the three drawers, and was just about to turn the chest of drawers onto it side, when he noticed something inside the chest. He put his hand inside and felt that something had been sellotaped to the very back. With a little effort he managed to remove a brown envelope, and to his amazement it contained a large amount of £20 notes. He called Dorothy and together they counted the money onto the table. '£500!' Rob gasped. 'I wonder who put that there!'

The couple made their way to the flat above the shop, and whilst Dorothy sat in front of the fire, Rob went to make a cup of tea. He'd only just left the room, when Dorothy turned her head to see an elderly man standing at her side. He looked ashen faced and very sad. Although Dorothy had been clairvoyant since she was a child, her spirit visitor looked as solid as any living person, and she was sure Rob would see him when he returned. 'Please find my daughter!' the man murmured. 'The money was for my funeral. Please find her!' Then, as Rob came back into the room, the man disappeared without trace. Dorothy explained to her husband exactly what had happened, and the following morning the couple went straight to the auction rooms to see if they could find out exactly where the chest of drawers originated. Although information of this nature is usually kept quite confidential, because Rob and Dorothy were well known to the auction house, a name and address in Toxteth was scribbled down.

The couple took a taxi straight to the address they had been given, but the house was now empty. After making a few enquiries, they were told that the man had indeed died, just as

Dorothy had said, and that his daughter lived a few doors away. As they stood on the step talking to the woman, she pointed to someone coming down the street pushing a pram. 'This is her coming now!' Dorothy approached the young woman, who looked lost and very distraught. Reluctantly she explained to the man's daughter exactly what had happened, and watched as her face lit up.

'I knew dad had put money away for his funeral,' sobbed the young woman. 'He was like that. We turned his house upside down, and couldn't find it anywhere. I had to borrow it from the bank. Oh, thank you so much!'

'Don't thank me,' smiled Dorothy, touching the young woman's hand affectionately. 'Thank your father. He was obviously upset, and didn't want you to have to pay for his funeral.'

Billy says: Sadly, both Dorothy and her husband Rob are no longer with us. Dorothy passed away in her husband's arms, at the age of 90; and Rob could see no point in going on without the love of his life. He died 12 months later.

24

Ghosts of Central Hall

When it was first built in 1905, The Grand Central .Hall in Renshaw Street, was a Wesleyan Chapel, a Methodist meeting place, and when the Philharmonic Hall was bombed during World War Two, concerts were then moved to this magnificent building. In the 1960s it sadly became the 'Dole', and the epicentre for the all the unemployed. However, in the 1940s this fine old building was used for important Spiritualist meetings, and it was here that the famous veteran medium, Estelle Roberts gave her incredibly impressive demonstration of mediumship to a capacity audience. Estelle Roberts was known the world over for her trance mediumship, and audiences would be amazed as the physical appearance of this eloquent speaker was dramatically transformed, when her Spirit Guide, Red Cloud spoke through her.

In 2001, The Grand Central Hall was also The Barcelona Nightclub, and today is the new home for 'Quiggins' New Age Shopping Centre, visited by people from all over the world. But, what about the 'spooky' goings on at the hall?

In the days when the hall was the 'Dole', the ghost of a man who became affectionately known as 'Limpy', was frequently seen roaming its corridors when the building was closed for business. When office staff approached him, he would simply disappear into thin air. The ghostly figure of the limping man was believed to be a caretaker who worked at the hall during the 1940s. He had apparently lost his leg during the Second World War, and pensioned out of the army, was given a job at The Grand Central Hall as caretaker and odd job man. One of the noticeable things about Limpy was the pungent smell he would always leave behind once he had disappeared.

The ghostly figure of a lady in a long white Victorian dress and large floppy hat has also been seen roaming through the corridors. Witnesses have all said the 'White Lady', as she has become known, looks as though she is lost, and has a distraught look on her face. She too just disappears without trace. Over the years a young boy in Edwardian clothes has also been seen wandering alone through the hall. He appears to see what he is looking for, and then just runs off into nothingness.

Billy says: As a medium and paranormal observer, I would expect all historical building to have their ghosts, images and reflections of things that have been, no more than that! After all, like people, buildings too have their memories, don't you think?

25

Haunted Furniture

It's impossible to tell what memories old pieces of furniture hold within their wooden structures, or what secrets they have kept over the years about the things to which they have borne witness. Can you ever know exactly what the antique sideboard you bought at auction has seen during its lifetime, and whether it has silently watched as a grisly crime took place? What happens to the furniture in the room where a bloody crime has been committed? Have you ever wondered, because I have!

Two of the following stories we related to me by readers of the first Spooky Liverpool, and the third story happened to a friend of my father's.

THE HAUNTED WARDROBE

The house where John and Violet Carney had lived for three years was over 100 years old, and they had meticulously kept the décor as near to the style of the day as possible. It was good that they both loved antiques, and so care was taken when furnishing their home with the correct period pieces. The only item of furniture they had never been able to find was a wardrobe large enough to fit into the alcove in their spacious bedroom, and when they finally located one in an Antique Emporium not far from where they lived, Violet was over the moon with excitement. It was delivered at the weekend to the home in Walton, and fitted perfectly into the large recess facing their bed. The wardrobe was double-fronted and made of mahogany and had a large mirror in the centre. Once Violet had applied a couple of coats of polish and a little elbow grease, the wardrobe shone like new. Before deciding whose clothes would go where, Violet gave the inside of the wardrobe the once over, just to make certain it was clean. She noticed something painted either side of the wardrobe on the back. As the writing had faded with time, she quickly turned on the light to inspect what was written more closely. On one side was written the name Julia, and on the other side the name William was just about readable. Violet felt a shiver of sadness pass through as she thought about the people who had owned it in the past.

It had been in place for a few days, when they both woke up in the middle of the night. They were not sure what had broken their sleep, and dismissed it as being noise from the traffic on the busy main road outside. Violet lay there for a few moments tossing and turning, and then John sat up. 'Can't you sleep either?' she said, yawning. 'It's difficult getting back to sleep once you've been disturbed.'

'Yeah! I know!' said John sitting up. Although some light filtered into the room from the streetlights outside, the couple's bedroom was comparatively dark. But then, Violet noticed a bright light shining as if from in the wardrobe mirror, and tried to locate the source of the unusual anomaly. Neither of them could work out where exactly the light was coming from, and it seemed, to all intents and purposes, to be shining from the mirror itself. 'Can't be,' mumbled John, 'It's probably reflecting from something outside.' They sat back on the bed for a few minutes, their eyes moving from one side of the room to the other, but they were still baffled.

'That's a puzzle!' remarked Violet, tiredly. 'Have you seen the time?' she pointed to the clock beside the bed. It was 3.30am. 'It's a good job it's Sunday. We can have a lie in!'

As Violet and John snuggled down beneath the blankets, they both noticed that the light suddenly grew brighter before disappearing completely, and looked just like the headlights of a car passing by. They both sat bolt upright, and were amazed to see the reflection of a lady in Edwardian clothes, staring out of the mirror at them. John quickly reached for the light and the woman's reflection disappeared.

'What the hell was that?' John said, swinging his legs over the side of the bed. 'Did you see that?'

'Of course I bloody well saw it!' Violet climbed out of bed and walked across the room towards the wardrobe, and then held her face close to the mirror. But all she could see was her own reflection and no more. Not knowing what to make of it, the couple climbed back into bed, turned off the light and settled down for the night. The following morning at breakfast, John was telling his teenage children about the spooky phenomenon. 'Spooky!' laughed Karen, the couple's 17-year-old daughter, 'as long as whatever it is stays in your room and doesn't come into mine!'

'I don't know why you want old furniture anyway,' said 19-year-old Mark, dismissing the whole thing completely. 'You don't know where it's been!'

Although John was extremely sceptical about anything connected to the supernatural, Violet totally believed in such things, and had in the past visited mediums. Not another word was said about the subject, and as they were all going to their caravan in Wales for a couple of days, the matter was forgotten.

The family were away for three days, and didn't return until late on Wednesday night. John carried their bags upstairs and was surprised when he saw the wardrobe door wide open, the mirror cracked in two places, and all the clothes strewn across the bedroom. Thinking for a moment that the house had been burgled, he called his wife.

'What the hell's been going on here?' Violet sat on the edge of the bed, unable to believe what she could see. 'The rest of the house is ok! So we haven't had burglars.' The couple sat in silence for a few moments, before John jumped angrily to his feet.

'That's it!' he snapped. 'It's going. First thing tomorrow I'll get someone to come and take it away.'

'Don't be silly!' huffed Violet. 'We'll never find another one to fit so snugly. The mirror can be replaced. Besides, spirits can't harm you! And anyway, I love it.'

'Don't care, it's going, and that's that,' said John.

Violet knew full well that she always had the last word, and John always did as she said. Before going down stairs, she gathered all the clothes that had seemingly been thrown around the room, and hung them neatly once again in the wardrobe. As she hung John's suit inside the wardrobe, she was suddenly overwhelmed by a strong fragrance. It was a smell that she was not familiar with. Her thoughts drifted for a moment, and she turned her back on the wardrobe to retrieve some items of clothing from the bed. She suddenly felt uncomfortable, as though someone was standing behind her. She thought John had walked into the room, and swung round to see. She got the fright of her life when she saw a woman standing in front of the wardrobe, a solemn look on her face. The woman was attired in a long Edwardian dress with a high fitted collar, and her dark hair was pulled neatly into a bun at the back of her head. For a moment she froze to the spot, and couldn't even find the voice to call her husband. The woman suddenly disappeared, leaving behind the sweet fragrance she had smelt previously.

Violet began to wonder about the wardrobe, and that maybe her husband was right after all, and that perhaps they should get rid of it.

After discussing it at some length with John, their minds we made up, it had to go! Although they had no definite proof, they wondered if the woman they had seen was Julia Wallace, the wife of William Wallace, (the man from the Pru, as he was known) and whether the spirit of Julia had somehow attached herself to the wardrobe in an effort to find the real perpetrator of her murder. Nonetheless, they got rid of the wardrobe and replaced it with a fitted one.

THE HAUNTED MIRROR

Although they lived in a fairly modern house, built in the mid-1960s, Ann and Phil Watts had a mixture of furniture styles in their detached house in Crosby. The furniture was mostly modern, but they did acquire the odd Victorian piece, like the large mirror that looked perfect above the mantel in the lounge. They'd bought the mirror in an antique shop in Chester, and although it was quite expensive, in its day it had obviously come from a grand house. Phil was certain that the old mirror had once been attached to a large sideboard or some other similar piece of furniture, but Ann didn't mind, it was exactly what they had been looking for.

The ornate mirror had been in place for a few days, when Ann decided that the light in the lounge was ideal in which to apply her makeup before going to Phil's mothers. She had always been very particular about her make-up, and like most women never liked distractions when putting it on. Phil was upstairs getting ready, and Ann had finished her make-up and was just about to brush her hair, when she saw a fiendish face grinning over her shoulder. She dropped the brush in fright and swung round to face whoever it was, but there was no one there. She was shaking and could feel her heart pounding inside her chest. She frantically ran from the room and called her husband from the bottom of the stairs. Phil thought Ann had had one of her turns, or perhaps hurt herself. He dashed downstairs to see if she was alright. 'You won't believe....' she gabbled, pointing into the lounge. 'Take a look!' Phil was always calm in a crisis and was never fazed by anything whatsoever. He thought she had seen a mouse or something, and walked calmly into the lounge, moving his eyes from one side to the other.

'What is it?' he said calmly. 'There's nothing here!'

Ann followed him into the room and pointed to the mirror.

When she'd calmed down, she told him what had happened. As expected Phil just laughed. 'Don't be silly! You probably imagined it.'

Ann was beginning to think her husband was right, and that she had imagined the grotesque face in the mirror. She breathed a long sigh and then laughed. After that experience Ann was reluctant to even comb her hair in that mirror, and for a while would not so much as glance at it. A few days had gone by, and Phil was working late. As it was mid November, it was a particularly frosty, and very foggy night. There was nothing on the TV, and so Ann decided to finish reading her magazine. She had forgotten all about her experience with the mirror, but when the light in the corner of the room began to flicker, for some reason her attention went to the mirror. She felt a sudden flash of panic, and her heart missed several beats. The light continued to flicker, and then went out completely leaving only one standard lamp on in the opposite corner of the lounge. Within seconds this too began to flicker, before finally going out, leaving the room completely in darkness. Now Ann really did panic and couldn't take her eyes from the mirror above the fireplace. Without moving her gaze from the mirror, she quickly stood up and moved towards the lounge door. The mirror suddenly began to glow with an intense, throbbing light, and eerie shadows danced across the floor of the lounge. The grotesque face she had seen in the mirror on that first night appeared again, its bulging fiendish eyes glaring at Ann from below its throbbing surface. She tried to open the lounge door to make a hasty retreat, but it would not open. Not taking her eyes from the mirror, she struggled frantically to open the door, but there was no use, it would not budge. Ann stood with her back to the door, watching helplessly as the horribly deformed figure of a man climbed down from the mirror above the mantel. 'No...' she screamed as loudly as she possibly could. 'Please...help me...' She watched as the grotesque figure limped slowly towards her, his bulging eyes glaring menacingly as he pointed accusingly at her as she now cowered in the corner of the room. He was no more than three feet away from her, and all that she could do was watch helplessly as he clawed at the space in front of him, eager to sink his long dirty nails into her flesh. 'No! Please... ' she pleaded. 'No...'

'Wake up, love,' a distant voice echoed inside her head. 'It's only me.' Ann opened her eyes to see Phil standing over her. She had fallen asleep on the settee and it had all been a dream, a very horrible dream – or, had it?

THE HAUNTED DRESSING TABLE

The beautifully crafted Victorian dressing table looked just right in Clare's front bedroom, and even though her husband Neil was not keen on antique furniture, he did have to agree. As the couple slept in the back, more spacious room, he wasn't really that bothered anyway.

Although the dressing table had been re-varnished at some time, it was still a fine old piece, and the couple both agreed that at £300 it was a bargain.

Below the nicely shaped mirror there were four drawers, and at the very back of one of these, neatly hidden, there was even a secret draw. Clare filled the drawers with all her make-up, and she used the front bedroom as her own personal dressing room. Neil was quite happy, and at least she was out of his and allowed him more freedom when the couple were getting ready for a night out.

After a particularly long day, Clare and Neil decided to have an early night. Neil's head had no sooner touched the pillow than he was fast asleep. Clare felt quite restless and was unable to sleep, and so just lay there mentally going over the list of things she had to do the following day whilst Neil was at work. Her thoughts were suddenly interrupted when she thought she could hear voices coming from the front bedroom. Not wanting to disturb her husband, she crept quietly out of bed, tiptoed the short distance down the landing and stood quietly outside the front bedroom door. Sure enough she could hear a woman's voice talking, and then a man's voice responding. She felt as though a window had been left open and a cold chill passed over her. She slowly pushed the bedroom door ajar and peeped inside, but the bedroom was empty. Thinking that she had been hearing things, probably because she was over tired, she closed the bedroom door, and then made her way back to her bedroom, where Neil was snoring loudly. She herself soon fell into a deep sleep, but was woken by a crashing sound. Neil too woke up at the same time. 'What the hell was that?' he mumbled, climbing tiredly out of bed. Clare nervously followed her husband, and they both stopped outside the front bedroom door and listened. There was another loud noise and, expecting to be confronted by burglars, Neil pushed the door wide open, and then readied himself to tackle whoever was there. Although the room was empty, the antique dressing table had seemingly been slung across the room by some invisible force, with the drawers and mirror lying strewn all over the floor. The couple couldn't believe what they were seeing, and all that they could do was just stand there, mouths open. 'What the hell's happened here?' blurted Neil incredulously. 'I don't understand it!'

Not really knowing what they expected to find, they checked all around the room, but there was no explanation for the spontaneous phenomenon. Neil helped his wife to put the dressing table back together, and then they went back to bed. When they got up the following morning, the first thing they did was to check the front bedroom. To their great surprise the antique dressing table had been thrown about the bedroom again, with the drawers and mirror strewn all over the floor. The couple decided immediately that the dressing table had to go, and whatever was causing the telekinetic phenomena, they did not want it to happen in their home. Not wanting to suffer the same frightening experience, that afternoon Neil borrowed his friend's van and assigned the Victorian dressing table to the rubbish tip where it belonged.

Billy says: The haunted dressing table remained a mystery to Ann and Neil, and they did wonder if it had caught someone's eye at the refuse tip, just as it had caught Ann's. Maybe it is now in someone else's bedroom! I wonder too!

26

Curses from World War Two

Although collectors of military artefacts can today find nearly all that they are looking for on Ebay, the online market place, the more serious collectors seek out the specialist dealers, who sell those hard-to-find items for the discerning collector of military souvenirs. As World War Two was over 60 years ago now, it is becoming more difficult to find certain military pieces. Nonetheless, dealers of such military artefacts are perhaps only known to the serious collector. One such shop could be found in Walton, until it closed in the late seventies. The proprietor, Colin, was a mine of information, and although his personal expertise is primarily about military Dress-swords, there isn't anything he doesn't know about First and Second World War collectables. This is a true story and involves a Second World War rifle.

Colin used to buy and sell anything from medals to uniforms, badges to helmets. One day an elderly man wondered into his shop with a few miscellaneous items to sell. One particular object that caught Colin's eye was a bolt-action Second World War army issue rifle. Apart from the obvious fact that the gun had been demobilised, it was in as near pristine condition as you would expect of an artefact that had survived World War Two.

The gun stood in a place of pride at the back of the shop, and although there was a lot of interest in the item, nobody actually bought it.

The rifle had been fixed firmly to the wall so everyone who came into the shop had a clear view of it. When Colin opened up the next morning, the first thing he noticed was that the rifle was lying on the counter. He had to think if he had removed it the night before, maybe to show a customer, and had perhaps had forgotten to return it to its fixture on the wall behind the counter. He was sure he hadn't, but no sooner had he returned the rifle to its fixture on the wall when he saw something out of the corner of his eye. Thinking it was an intruder, he swung his head round to see a young soldier standing at the end of the counter, holding out his hand as though he wanted Colin to pass the rifle to him. It hadn't crossed Colin's mind that the young soldier might have been a ghost, but when the ghostly figure disappeared he went icy cold.

There was usually an extremely fast turnover with most of the military artefacts that came into his possession, and the gun was no exception. Within two days it had caught somebody's eye, and the gun was sold. Although it was a rare piece, Colin was glad to get rid of it. He thought that was the last he'd seen of the rifle, until one afternoon the elderly man who had bought it walked into the shop carrying something wrapped in a couple of bin bags. 'Will you take this bloody rifle back?' he almost pleaded, placing the package on the counter. 'The missus wants me to get rid of it. She says we'll have no luck.'

Colin looked at the man's weather-beaten face and could see he was a little disturbed. 'Why? What's the matter?'

At first he seemed to be reluctant to say what the problem was, in case Colin laughed at him. 'I was going to make a frame for it so I could hang it on the wall in my study. I had left it on the table in my workshop at the bottom of the garden,' he paused, embarrassed. 'When I went in there was a young soldier standing there looking at the rifle. To be honest, Colin, you can have it back for nothing. I just want to get rid of it.' The elderly man did not even wait for him to respond, and just left the shop.

Colin held onto the rifle for a while, and the same ghostly soldier appeared twice after that. Eventually it was sold and that was the end of that, at least where Colin was concerned.

Billy says: Little do the collectors of such artefacts realise what has attached itself to the war relics they have collected. The energies of those who have died will always cling to things as well as people.

THE GHOSTLY RELIC FROM THE GREAT WAR

Liverpool Militaria is a small very select shop located at 17 Cheapside. This is perhaps one of the few shops of its kind, and its proprietor, Bill Tagg, is extremely knowledge about all things Militaria. Although Bill has a special interest in Samari swords, his shop is a veritable Aladdin's Cave, full of innumerable interesting First and Second World War collectables. People frequently wonder into Bill's shop either to browse or sometimes to sell items. Although the majority of things offered to him are of no special interest to him, on the odd occasion he is offered something that really catches his eye. One day a young man wondered into his shop carrying a bag of goodies, as Bill explained it. He explained to Bill that his father worked for the War Graves Authorities and frequently had to go to the Somme, the location of thousands of fatalities in the Great War. The young man went on to tell Bill that he frequently accompanied his father, and would spend many hours digging around in the trenches, to see what he could find. This was where the bag of miscellaneous artefacts he had brought for Bill Tagg to look at had been found. Bill emptied the contents of the bag onto the top of the counter, and immediately clapped eyes on the rusty remains of a rifle. Although the butt had long since gone, Bill had an eye for the potential of something like this, and had immediately decided what he would do with it.

The deal was done, and Bill put the gun in a cupboard in the back room for safekeeping. He had planned to restore it and then fix it in a glass-covered wooden frame. The last customer had just left, and the shop was silent. Bill decided to close early, and was just about to collect his coat from the office when he heard a sequence of loud noises, rather like distant explosions and men's voices calling. The noises were coming from the back room where he had put the old gun, and so he went to investigate. The cupboard in which he'd put it was fiercely vibrating, and a cacophony of explosions echoed through the small shop, one after another. Bill felt as though he was actually on a battlefield, and for a few moments the terror of actually being there really gripped him. The loud noises continued for a few minutes and then suddenly stopped. Bill couldn't wait to lock up for the night and make his way to his local for a pint before heading home.

He decided to let the First World War relic go to anyone who wanted it, and so placed it on show at the back of the counter. One of his regular customers called in to see if he'd got anything interesting in. Bill showed him the old rifle and the man immediately bought it. Although Bill felt a little guilty not telling the customer about the spooky phenomena, he was glad to see the back of it. Unfortunately, that wasn't the last he'd seen of the gun. A week later the man returned to try and persuade Bill to take it back. 'The wife wants me to get rid of it,' he insisted. 'We heard all kinds of explosions in the middle of the night, and the table I'd left the rifle on was vibrating like hell!'

Although Bill refused to take the relic back to the man, he did tell him all about his experience.

A few weeks later the man returned to tell Bill that he'd left the old rifle at his friend's, and he had had the very same experience.

'I'd take it to the tip!' advised Bill. 'It's obviously haunted! Anyway, I don't want it.'

Billy says: The last Bill Tagg had heard the man was still in possession of the gun, although he never mentioned the phenomena again. Bill wondered about all the other memorabilia in his shop. Maybe there were other ghosts, who perhaps only came out at night when he had locked up and gone home.

• **Should you be a collector of military memorabilia from the First and Second World Wars, go and see Bill Tagg at The Liverpool Militaria, 17 Cheap Side, (off Dale Street) in Liverpool city centre. There's nothing he doesn't know about the two wars.**

27

The First World War Angel of The Trenches

Bill Gardener had lied about his age to get into the army. It was 1914 and the war had just started and he desperately wanted to be with his 19-year-old brother, Sid, on the front line in France. Although he was only 15 years old, he looked at least 18 and had somehow managed to fool the army recruiting officials and bluff his way through the initial interview. Against his parents' protestations, Bill was on his way to France.

The reality of the war only really hit him when he actually set foot on the beaches of France. The smoke-filled air and the constant sounds of exploding mortars overwhelmed him with fear and panic and, for a short while, he almost wished he was back home with his mother and father and younger brother, Sam. But he wasn't, he was in France fighting for his country. Young people find it very difficult to believe in their own mortality but, despite this, every so often it dawned on him that he might even be killed in this war and never see his family again. It was too late now for Bill to change his mind and, although he could already feel the strong camaraderie amongst the other soldiers fighting beside him, in the face of the enemy, it was still every man for himself. Although he had joined up to be with his older brother, as yet, he had not seen him and began to wonder if he ever would.

Sitting in the freezing trenches in the dead of night, Bill tried desperately not to show the others just how terrified he really was. After all, as far as they were concerned he was a man and not a 15-

year-old boy, just out of school. Before going to sleep each night he said his prayers quietly, so that the other men could not hear him. He prayed for protection for himself and his brother and asked that they would be delivered safely back home and that the war would end quickly.

Within a few days, the fighting really began in earnest and men of all ages were lying dead and injured in the mud of the trenches all around him. Bill wanted to run but there was nowhere to run to, nowhere to hide. He was so frightened and bitterly regretted having lied about his age.

He had been in the trenches for about three weeks and already the fighting was fierce. The incessant noise was deafening, and the air in the trenches was so thin and acrid that he could hardly breathe. Suddenly there was a massive explosion and everything went black. He lay unconscious for a long time and came round to a scene of utter devastation. There were bloodied bodies strewn all over the trench and the stench was unbearable. He coughed painfully as he took in a lungful of thick, choking smoke. He struggled to clear his lungs and then fumbled to secure his gas mask on his face and pull himself clumsily to his feet. He felt so weak and could barely move one leg in front of the other, along the slippery duckboards of the trench.

His right leg felt soggy and wet and, judging by the pain in it, he guessed that it was bleeding and that he had sustained some sort of injury in the blast. He managed to make his way carefully along the line of his trench but as far as he could see, all his comrades were either dead or dying. He wasn't sure whether he was lucky to be alive, or whether an even more horrific death lay in store for him. He kept reminding himself that he was only 15 and trying to persuade himself that the Germans simply did not kill 15-year-old boys. But he knew this was not true.

Darkness soon descended and Bill was so exhausted that he made himself as comfortable as he could amidst the slimy chaos of the trenches and fell asleep. Within a few minutes he was woken by the loud cracks of gunfire and harsh German voices calling from no more than 10 yards away from the trench in which he was hiding. He quickly pulled himself to his feet and began to move as fast as he could through the darkness. He had no idea where he was heading and was guided only by instinct and sheer terror. He was convinced that he was either going to be killed, or even taken prisoner and left to die in some dreadful prisoner-of-war camp. He had never been so frightened in all his life and called out constantly for his brother, Sid.

Just as he realised that the German soldiers had entered the trench and had begun searching the rubble for signs of life, Bill noticed a light shining ahead of him and thought that perhaps one of his comrades had survived the attack and was being careless with his torch. He made his way towards the light and, to his surprise, he could see a young woman dressed in white. She had long fair hair and was carrying a lantern in one hand and beckoning for him to follow her with the other. Bill was afraid that the Germans would also see the light and checked to see if they were following, but there was no one there.

The young woman kept her distance from Bill but stopped every so often to make certain that he was still following her. Although he knew there was a possibility that she was leading him straight to the enemy, instinct alone forced him to keep moving in her wake.

Eventually she rounded a bend where one trench led into another and when Bill had also turned the corner, the young woman had disappeared completely.

He stopped to survey the darkness surrounding him but there was no sign of the young woman anywhere. He could feel his heart pounding like a drum inside his chest and was suddenly overwhelmed once again by fear. He felt helpless and completely lost. He fell to his knees in defeat and resigned himself to inevitable capture.

Suddenly, an English voice cut through the darkness and made Bill spring to his feet.

'Where are you?' he cried out. 'Keep calling so I can see where you are.'

'Over here!' The voice sounded loud and clear. 'We're over here!'

Bill moved carefully through the darkness in the direction of the voice and suddenly came upon three wounded men, sitting with their backs to the wall of the trench.

'I'm so pleased to see...' Bill stopped in mid sentence. 'I don't believe it!' he continued. Stooping to look more closely at the face of one of the men. 'Sid!'

It was indeed Bill's brother who had been calling him. Apart from having a slight wound on his left shoulder, he was alright. The two brothers had been reunited at last, thanks to the mysterious lady in white, who had guided him with her lantern, through the maze of trenches, to safety.

Bill and his brother were hospitalised for three weeks before returning to the front line. The two brothers were allowed to remain together for the rest of the war and, miraculously, both survived to return to Liverpool in 1918. Although Bill never found out who the lady in the trenches actually was, he never forgot her and always referred to her as the Angel in the Trenches.

Billy says: There are innumerable stories of a similar phenomenon, and many First and Second World War soldiers testified that they were guided through the trenches to safety. My grandfather was one such soldier, and he told the story of the Angel of the Trenches until the day he died in 1963.

28

THE MYSTERY OF HEATHER

Joe Lantrey always maintained that a pub was no place to meet a girl. He'd gone through a very acrimonious divorce, and had lost an awful lot of confidence as a consequence. He had allowed 12 months before considering himself 'on the market', so to speak, and now felt he was ready for a relationship. Joe had been a fireman for 20 years, and although he loved the job, he hated coming home to an empty house. He was quite surprised when he met Heather at the Grapes pub in Woolton. Although Joe was in his mid fifties, he had kept himself quite fit and had lost a lot of weight over the last six months. Heather was a stunner, Joe thought, unable to believe his luck when she chatted him up as he was ordering a round of drinks for him and his friends.

The woman, in her mid forties, had shoulder-length dark brown hair, and with no Liverpool accent, it was obvious she had come from a very good background. She politely declined his offer to join him and his friends for a drink. 'I can't stay, but thank you,' she said, 'I just popped in to see a friend. I think I must've missed her. Maybe we can meet up another time? But thank you'. Joe didn't think to ask for her phone number, but just scribbled his on a piece paper he'd found on top of the bar. 'I'll call you soon. Nice meeting you. And thank you so much.' He stood for few moments at the bar, mesmerised by her beauty, and stood watching her until she had disappeared through the pub door. He remarked to himself just how polite she was, and wondered why she kept saying thank you. Must be a nervous habit, he decided.

'A man could die of thirst!' One of his friends joked. 'What kept you?'

'I've just met the most beautiful woman in the whole world. Did you see her?'

Thinking he was drunk, his friend, Dave, shook his head. 'See who?'

'The girl I was talking to at the bar. She was beautiful. I gave her my number. I'm taking her for a drink, or maybe a meal.'

His friends just glanced sideways at each other, a disbelieving look on their faces. Joe knew they didn't believe him, but he didn't care. He just hoped she would call him sooner rather than later.

Heather did call him, and they arranged to meet in Woolton Village. 'Not in The Grapes!' she insisted. 'I know too many people there.'

'Me too!' agreed Joe, disappointed that his friends wouldn't get to meet her. 'We'll go somewhere for a bite to eat.'

As planned Heather met him by Sainsbury's and they took a taxi to a Chinese restaurant in nearby Allerton Road. Heather was good company and kept the conversation flowing all night. This was good for Joe as he was well out of practise. He really enjoyed himself and was hoping that she would want to see him again. He was quite taken aback when she asked if she could come back to his for a nightcap.

'Do you live far?'

'No, not really! Elm Hall Drive, off Queens Drive.' Joe was quite flustered, and all he could think about was whether or not the place was tidy. All his kids were grown up now, and he'd grown accustomed to living by himself. 'You'll have to excuse the mess though. I live the life of a bachelor and, unfortunately I'm very untidy – or, so my ex-wife used to say.'

They had a few more drinks at Joe's place, and they had discussed just about everything, when Heather noticed the time. 'It's 2am!' she gasped, placing her glass on the coffee table. 'I really must be going. Will you call me a taxi?'

'Of course,' said Joe reluctantly. 'But, you could always stay?' As soon as he realised what he had said, he stuttered an awkward apology. 'I have a spare room!'

'That would be nice. Thank you. I'm staying with my mother at the moment, and I never like to disturb her. Not that I make a habit of staying out late, you understand! And, thank you so much'.

Before they finally retired for the night, Joe made them both a warm drink, and they chatted a little more. At least he'd found out that she too was divorced, and that she had a fourteen-year-old son called Michael, and they both lived with her widowed mother off Menlove Avenue.

As his bed was more comfortable, Heather slept in his room.

Joe tossed and turned all night, unable to get Heather out of his mind. The following morning he was up bright and early. The kettle was on and the bread was in the toaster. He checked the time on the clock in the kitchen and it was ten precisely. 'She was obviously tired'. He smiled to himself, deciding to take her breakfast in bed. He knocked on the door a few times, each knock louder than the one before, but there was still no response. Joe eventually called her name before pushing the door open, but the room was completely empty. He was quite surprised to see that the bed looked as though it hadn't been slept in. He checked all over the house but there was no sign of Heather anywhere. She had obviously decided not to stay after all, and didn't have the common courtesy to even leave him a note. He sniffed at the air, but there wasn't even a trace of her sweet fragrance anywhere in the house.

Feeling quite rejected, and somewhat let down, he tried to put the incident from his mind, and decided not to mention it to his friends. They'd only laugh at him anyway, and probably make some silly remark.

The days went by and Joe's routine carried on in exactly the same way as it had for many years. Work, the pub and then bed, everyday the same as the other. A boring daily routine that seemed to Joe to be one long road to the grave. He rather enjoyed working nights though, at least then he was doing something worthwhile. Although he tried desperately to put Heather from his mind, the more he tried the more she kept coming into his thoughts. He couldn't stand it anymore, and decided to go to the address where she had said she lived with her mother and son, Michael.

As Joe turned the corner into the road where Heather lived, he recalled attending a fire there some years ago. He pulled up outside number 27, and then it suddenly dawned on him that this was the location of the fire in which an elderly woman and her daughter had died. He sat in his car for a few moments recalling the terrible incident in his mind. He had rescued a 14-year-old boy, the only survivor. An icy shiver passed through him, as he climbed out of his car and stood in front of the house. Although now completely refurbished, there was no mistaking that this was the place.

He enquired at the house, and although it was obviously now occupied by another family, the woman living there knew almost everything about those who had died in the fire. 'Mrs Slater and her daughter, Heather died in the fire. Michael, Heather's son, was rescued by one of the firemen, and he now lives in America.'

Before driving away Joe sat in his car, numb and completely confused. He couldn't believe that Heather had been a ghost. At least he understood why she kept saying 'Thank you,' at the end of every sentence. He breathed in deeply and released a long sigh. 'I knew it was too good to be true!'

29

Ghostly Penny Lane

As a medium I do have to say that nowhere is exempt from ghostly visitors, and wherever you go you can rest assured that unseen eyes will be watching. Since establishing the northwest's very first Centre for Psychic and Spiritual Studies in Rodney Street, in 1983, we have been in numerous locations. Although sadly the Thought Workshop closed down some years ago now, The Billy Roberts Paranormal Study Centre opened in Penny Lane, made famous by the Beatles' song of the same name. The centre was located at 112 Penny Lane and was more or less opposite my father's childhood home, number 126. This is the only double-fronted house in Penny Lane, and was home to William Walmsly and Jane Roberts, my grandparents, the founders of the famous pet store, City Pets, originally located in Market Street, a narrow cobbled street that ran at the back of the first St John's Market, and relocated later in the new precinct. Sadly, the famous pet shop has closed, but the family's ghostly legacy apparently still lives on in Penny Lane. Although my father and his brother, George, got married and left the family home many years ago, their sister, Louise remained there until the day she died. She was a formidable character and, by all accounts, an unknown quantity. She lived into her late nineties, and in later years became a recluse. She was very eccentric and, unfortunately, suffered from Alzheimer's disease, making life for her even more miserable. She had driven everyone away, and only allowed her brother George to visit her, which he did every week without fail. Although the Victorian house was extremely spacious, Louise was confined to the downstairs front room, where she was eventually found dead.

Auntie Louise died, around 1989, and the house stood empty for some time whilst a buyer was sought. It was eventually sold and immediately converted into flats. Only my wife, Dolly, knew of my connection with the house, and yet over the years several people have called to my office seeking help with alleged poltergeist activity in the house. There have been reports of many different kinds of phenomena at the house, including telekinetic activity, (the movement of objects such as furniture etc), apparitions and lights turning on and off by themselves. I would have been forgiven for thinking that 'eccentric' Auntie Louise had been responsible for all the so-called 'disturbance' in the house, had my father not told me about the 'spooky goings on' there when he was a child. In fact, when my father was a young boy disembodied voices would frequently echo through the house, and furniture could often be seen moving across the floor, without any human intervention. My father once saw the ghostly figure of a sea captain standing on the top of the stairs, a look of mischief on his bearded face. This was purported to be the man who had lived there before the Roberts family. So violent was the phenomena at times, that my grandmother called in a priest to 'exorcise' the unwanted ghostly visitors. The priest apparently came prepared with the bell, book and the candle, but when he encountered the poltergeist, he fled just as eagerly as he had come.

My father used to tell me that he would be afraid to sleep without a nightlight, and even then he and his brother would be terrified by the ghostly figures walking across the room. For a while the house seemed to be silent, until one day a student living there came to my office seeking help. He was experiencing all sorts of paranormal activity and was getting to that point where he was quite disturbed. As I was busy, he was asked to call back later. Needless to say, he did not call again.

Today, the grand old house in Penny Lane is still divided into flats and, I often wonder if the ghostly visitors are still there, playing their mischievous games.

Billy says: Until the house was sold after my Auntie Louise's death, my Uncle George, my brother and I owned the house. I must say, although full of family memories, the house itself seemed to have its own memories; memories of bygone days. My father always maintained that 126 Penny Lane was a very happy house, and although the Roberts family shared it with a host of disembodied souls, he never really thought any evil prevailed there.

30

The Ghost of Greenbank Park

In the school summer holidays I used to love spending the afternoon on the rowing boats on Greenbank Park lake. Summers seemed to be so much hotter then, and the beautiful Victorian park was always was full of parents with their children, and people just lying in the sun. Unlike today, in those days fishing was forbidden, and anyone caught doing so would receive an immediate fine.

For those of you who don't know Greenbank Park, it is situated close to the borders of Sefton Park, and was originally a part of the Rathbone Estate. In 1788, the Rathbone family moved into Greenbank House, with the sole intention of using it as a holiday home. However, they liked living there so much that they eventually made it their permanent residence, and frequently played host to many distinguished visitors. The Rathbone family in fact lived there until 1940, and became known for their kindness towards the 'poor' people of Liverpool.

In 1897 the Rathbone family sold a piece of land, for the sum of £13,000 to Liverpool Corporation, which was turned into parkland, and is today known as Greenbank Park. The walled garden is allegedly all that remains of the Rathbone family's original estate, and has been featured in many TV and film productions.

However, as one would expect, there is a more ghostly side to Greenbank Park. Over the years there have been many fatalities at the park, ranging from accidents to suicides. And it is really only over the past 20 years that railings have been erected around the park. Prior to that easy access could be gained into the Victorian Park, at anytime, day or night.

In the 1960s, Lawrence Pilch and his two friends, Martin and Gary Gardener frequently had a midnight sojourn in Greenbank Park, on a 'rave' as they called it. Even in the middle of winter it was quite peaceful, and apart from the odd tramp sleeping on a bench, there was never anyone around. Lawrence, or Lol as his friends knew him, had spent the night with his girlfriend, Debbie, at a club in town, and had decided to introduce her to Greenbank Park in the dead of night. 'We often come here,' he boasted, knowing full well that he wouldn't dare go to the park at night by himself. 'It's so peaceful.'

'I think it's quite spooky,' she remarked, holding on tightly to Lawrence's arm. They'd just rounded the lake, and were now on the side opposite Greenbank Road. Here it was quite secluded and peaceful, and the two decided to sit on the bench overlooking the lake. A crescent moon cast uneven shadows across the water, and the occasional hoot of an owl set the eerie scene perfectly. Lawrence simply enjoyed the fact that his girlfriend was so frightened, that she held on tightly to him all the time.

They sat for quite some time just listening to the sounds of the night, and watching the light playing eerily across the lake, when they noticed two figures walking down the path towards them. At first Lawrence thought that the moonlight had caused the silhouettes of the two approaching figures to shimmer in the darkness, but as they drew nearer he could see that this was not the case. Debbie and Lawrence sat forward on the bench, unable to believe their eyes. A man and woman attired in Victorian clothes, casually walked past them, seemingly completely unaware of their presence. The couple watched in amazement as the man and woman disintegrated before their eyes. Realising that they had seen two ghosts, Debbie and Lawrence sprang to their feet and left the park much quicker than when they had entered it. Needless to say, Lawrence had been sufficiently frightened never to come back to Greenbank Park at night.

Although the rowing boats have long since gone from the park's lake, whilst walking through the picturesque area at night, many people have witnessed a ghostly rowing boat sailing on the lake, and have watched in amazement as it disappears into nothingness. Others have witnessed the ghostly appearance of a young lady in a long white dress, holding out a pleading hand, before finally disappearing into the night.

Billy says: Sitting in any darkened place for long enough, is just like sitting in front of a huge TV screen. Whether or not you are psychic, the night will always 'come alive' with images and other things of the past. However, it behoves you to take great care; should they notice you watching them, then who knows what will happen...

31

The Ghostly Funeral Cortage

Frank Linden had always been close to his mother, Margaret, and was devastated when he learned that she had been diagnosed with lung cancer and the prognosis was not good. She was a widow and lived with her sister Elsie, in Wavertree and Frank lived in Hayfield Street, Anfield, a few miles away. Margaret had grown up in Anfield and she had often told her son stories of the days when she was a child playing in the streets where he now lived with his wife, Jean, and two daughters, Barbara and Jenny.

Frank and his family had only been living in the corner house in Hayfield Street for six months and had quickly settled into the friendly community. The neighbours had been very helpful when they moved in and even offered to help carry furniture up the narrow staircase to the bedrooms. It was so friendly that Frank and Jean felt as though they had always lived there and the girls even looked forward to going to school for the first time.

Frank's mother appeared to respond to her treatment and it looked as though she was going into remission. He knew he could not have his mother forever, but he just prayed that she would survive for a few more years, if only to see her granddaughters grow up.

It was a warm Saturday evening in July 1986 and Frank and Jean had taken the children to spend the evening with their grandmother in Wavertree. She appeared to be in good spirits and was talking about the future with a positive attitude. Frank could see that there had been some improvement, if only in her psychological state and he began to feel cautiously optimistic. He worked at Ford and was on the early shift that Sunday, so they left his mother's at about nine o'clock so that he could have a shower and an early night. At about three o'clock the next morning, something woke him from his intense sleep. Jean also was quite restless and eventually opened her eyes.

'What's the matter, love?' she asked, putting a comforting hand on his back.

Something woke me up,' he said, rubbing his eyes. 'I know it's ridiculous but it sounded like horses' hooves on the cobbles outside.'

'What cobbles?' laughed Jean. 'There aren't any cobbles on the street. You must have been dreaming. There aren't any horses around here either for that matter.'

As he slowly came to his senses, he suddenly realised what he had been saying.

'You're right, love,' he whispered, swinging his legs to the floor from beneath the bed covers. 'I must've been dreaming. But I'll just take a look anyway.'

He crossed over towards the window and peeped through the curtains, but the street was deserted, just as he had expected.

'Come back to bed, love,' said Jean in a reassuring voice. 'You're probably worried about your mum.'

'I suppose so,' he yawned and climbed back into bed and pulled the covers over himself again. 'You go back to sleep,' he said to Jean, 'I'll just lie here for a while.'

The night passed very slowly and Frank had not slept at all by the time the alarm clock went off at five o'clock and he climbed wearily out of bed.

'I'll get up when you've had your shower,' Jean said, still half asleep. 'I'll make you some breakfast.'

'No,' said Frank, 'you stay in bed, I'm not going into work today. I've decided to take a few weeks off. The doctor will give me a note I'm sure.'

This was not like her husband and Jean was immediately

concerned about him and knew that he was more worried about his mother than he was prepared to admit.

The following night Frank and Jean stayed up until the early hours talking. The girls were fast asleep and the streets outside were quiet. Eventually, Jean yawned and stretched her arms above her head.

'I'm tired now, love, I think I'll go up.'

Frank agreed that it was late and decided to join her. But again, at around three o'clock, he was woken up by the sound of horses' hooves on a cobbled street. He nudged Jean to listen and they both lay there in the darkness. It was silent for a few moments and then they both distinctly heard the sound of a horse, trotting across a cobbled surface. They sprang out of bed simultaneously and looked through the window into the dimly lit street, not in anyway prepared for the sight which greeted their eyes. In the street below was a black, plumed horse pulling an ornate Victorian funeral carriage and a man, dressed smartly in black with a top hat, leading the horse by its reins. They both shivered as the whole image faded into nothingness when the carriage reached the corner of the street by their house. Frank immediately switched on the light and sat on the edge of the bed in stunned silence.

'So, I wasn't dreaming after all,' he said, after a while. 'What do you suppose it was?'

'I don't know,' answered Jean, equally bewildered. 'There must have been an undertakers close by.'

They both replayed the whole ghostly scene over and over in their minds. Frank was the first to speak.

'Let's get back in bed,' he said, trying to dismiss the whole experience from his mind. 'Don't know about you, but I'm absolutely shattered.'

'Yeah, me too,' responded Jean. 'We'll talk about it in the morning. Maybe one of the neighbours can throw some light on it.'

The first neighbour whom Jean asked about the incident had lived in the street for over 35 years. She had to admit that she had neither heard nor seen anything remotely ghostly in all that time.

'Although some say the King Harry pub round the corner is haunted.' She went on. 'But I don't really know.'

The following night, Frank and Jean were half expecting the ghostly cortege again. They sat up in bed talking until well after midnight but, at that point, they were both so tired that they fell asleep and did not wake up again until the following morning at eight o'clock.

A few day passed by and then Frank's mother had been taken into hospital for more tests. That night the two of them were woken at about three o'clock by the same sound of a horse trotting across a cobbled surface. They both peered nervously at the now familiar scene through the curtains and, because the moonlight shone quite brightly, they could see the figure of the man leading the horse quite clearly. This time, the horse and funeral carriage stopped almost outside their house. Their neighbour had told Jean to ring her the next time they saw the ghostly apparition, but they were both so mesmerised by the scene outside their window, that they could not bring themselves to move from their position. The ghostly cortege remained a little longer on this occasion, before eventually evaporating, just as before, into nothingness.

Frank and Jean were completely unsettled until daylight shone through their bedroom curtains once again. Jean could not help thinking that the apparition was in some way connected with Frank's mother and he could not get the mental image out of his mind and it left him with a morbid, oppressive feeling, which stayed with him all day.

Two weeks passed by, during which time they had seen the phantom horse and carriage several times and, on each occasion, it had remained a little longer than the time before. By now, both Frank and Jean were totally exhausted and fell fast asleep each night as soon as they had climbed into bed. At three o'clock one morning they were both woken up with a start by three heavy knocks on their bedroom door. Thinking that it was one of the girls, Frank sprang quickly out of bed but there was no one there. He crept into his daughters' room and found that they were fast asleep. By the time he arrived back in the bedroom, Jean was sitting bolt upright in bed, looking startled.

'Shush!' she murmured, staring straight ahead, with her finger pressed to her lips, 'Listen.'

They could hear the horse trotting across the cobbles and they both crossed over to the window and looked through the curtains. The carriage had stopped outside their front door and they could now see a coffin on it for the first time, covered in flowers. Seconds later, the phantom funeral carriage had disappeared completely, leaving Frank and Jean feeling shaken and wondering if it was some sort of omen.

From experience they knew that sleep was impossible, so they were just on their way downstairs to make a cup of tea when the telephone rang. They looked at each other, expecting the worst. Frank's brother, Roger, was on the other end of the line.

'Mum's dead,' he said solemnly. 'She died at three o'clock.'

But Frank and Jean already knew.

Billy says: Although I know this story is true, and has been verified by various people, my only concern is why were the couple put through all that anguish and pain? Over the years there have been numerous ghostly sightings in and around Hayfield Street in Anfield. Do you have a story to tell? If so, contact me.

32

Spooky Drawings

Having been psychic since I was a child, it is really difficult for me to know exactly what it would be like not to be psychic. To a sceptic all this would probably seem a little far-fetched and fanciful, but the truth is I do not know any different. Ever since I can remember seeing so-called 'dead' people was commonplace to me, and up until the age of 10 I thought that everyone was the same as me. Of course, this was not the case! Although the majority of people view the idea of Spirit Guides with ridicule, and others the subject of many jokes, since my early childhood I have been acquainted with a discarnate individual I came to know as 'Tall Pine', a Native American who frequently visited me when I was alone. Only I knew what Tall Pine looked like, and my relationship with him remains just as strong even today. In the mid 1970s I had a consultation with Mary Duffy, an international medium from Edinburgh. We'd never met before, and yet she seemed to be able to produce many personal details about my life. She even relayed messages from my father who died in 1970. Mary astounded me by telling me all about Tall Pine, and even gave me his name. In fact, she kept saying his name over and over again, and said 'Tall Pine is telling me that if you get the opportunity to have a consultation with a psychic artist, he will make sure that you will get a drawing of him.'

I left the consultation with a mixture of feelings. I was so happy with all that she had said, but I knew that if I did see a psychic artist and he did not produce Tall Pine's likeness, then my faith in my work would be shattered completely.

Six months later I was fortunate to have a consultation with one of the world's greatest exponents of psychic art, Ivor James (now deceased.) As soon as I entered the little room in which he was working, I was suddenly overwhelmed with apprehension and nervousness. I'd no sooner sat down in front of him when he lowered his eyes and began to sketch, raising his eyes occasionally over his bifocals to look over my shoulder. 'You know who I am drawing, don't you?' he said, with a matter-of-fact tone.

'Yes,' I stuttered, 'I mean, I hope so.' I just hoped he would draw Tall Pine, at least as I knew him, and not someone unknown to me.

I listened nervously to his pencil as it scratched the surface of the paper, at that point knowing that my whole future as a medium was held in the tip of Ivor James' pencil. I waited with bated breath and watched as he paused for a moment to inspect his finished work. He sprayed some fixer across the paper and then held the finished work in front of me. 'Tall Pine!' I gasped, with excitement.

'Absolutely,' he said. 'Who else?'

Clutching the drawing of Tall Pine close to my chest, I left Ivor James in an almost trance-like state, unable to believe that I had had Tall Pine's likeness confirmed. I was now more convinced than ever that Tall Pine was not a figment of my imagination, and that no matter what anyone said, I knew that Spirit Guides do exist, and that Tall Pine was still watching over me. Ivor James in fact became a friend and remained so until the day he died. The drawing of Tall Pine still hangs on the wall in my study, his solemn face looking the same as ever.

33

The Haunted Violin

After the Second World War, many servicemen found themselves without work, and some even took to busking on the streets. Joe Lawrenson had lost a leg in France, and now that the war was over he had found it very difficult to get work anywhere. He had inherited his father's musical ability and had played the violin since he was eight years old. There were a few buskers here and there on the streets of Liverpool, and so Joe decided to give it a try. After all, he had nothing to lose, and with two daughters and a wife to feed, he had everything to gain. He'd had the same violin since he was a child, and although he was a little out of practise, his fingers soon began to move across the strings with great ease. Busking proved to be quite profitable, and although Joe never stayed in the same place for more than a day, he quickly learned which areas were the most generous.

Even though Liverpool was still recovering from the war in the early fifties, city shoppers would still find a few pennies to throw into Joe's hat. He had been busking for over nine years, and would have continued quite happily, had the doctor not told him that he had to go into hospital for tests on his heart. Sadly, Joe died of a heart attack just after being discharged from hospital, and his violin's melodic tones were no longer heard on the streets of Liverpool. As Joe's granddaughter, Joyce, had obviously inherited his love of the violin, it seemed only right that she should have his much loved instrument. Joe had been teaching her, and although she was only five years old, it was clear to everyone that she had an aptitude for the violin.

One afternoon whilst little Joyce was at school, Joe's daughter, Maggie, was sitting in the living room having a well-deserved cup of tea, when she thought she heard the sound of violin music coming from upstairs. She knew her daughter was at school, so it couldn't be her. Maggie went upstairs to investigate, but when she had reached the landing at the top of the stairs, the music faded into nothingness. Maggie pushed open the door and saw that the violin was lying on her daughter's bed. 'I told her to put it in the case when she'd finished playing it,' she tutted, shaking her head impatiently, as she retrieved the violin from the bed and placed it securely in the tatty case. Although now quite old, the violin was precious to Maggie, and she had insisted that her daughter should look after it. Joy was adamant that she always put it in the case after she finished playing it, and Maggie believed her. Maggie heard the spooky music several times after that, and each time she investigated it, the violin was lying on the bed, just like the first time.

The ghostly phenomenon seemed to become more frequent over the months, and Maggie and her husband were beginning to be a little unnerved by it, until one day their daughter announced, 'Don't worry, it's only granddad making sure that we don't forget him!'

'What do you mean?' Maggie was puzzled by her daughter's statement.

'He comes to see me sometimes, and says he wants me to play just like him. He said he misses his violin, and hopes I don't mind him playing it.'

Maggie was speechless. She knew her daughter couldn't make up such a story, and in some way felt comforted to know that her father was still around, and still able to play his violin.

Billy says: This is a true story, and although no longer a little girl, Joyce still plays her grandfather's violin. As for the phenomenon of the ghostly music, this too continues even to this day. Joyce also told me that she no longer sees granddad Joe, but she always knows when he's around.

34

Mysterious Goings on at St George's Hall

The magnificent architecture of St George's Hall is known the world over, and cost approximately £300,000 to build. It was designed by architect Harvey Lonsdale Elmes, and took 10 years to build, opening its doors to the public in 1854. This grand building was once the Crown Court, in which many infamous murderers were tried and either imprisoned or sentenced to death. Accused of poisoning her husband, James Maybrick, who many believe to have been the infamous Jack the Ripper, Florence Maybrick was tried and sentenced to death at St George's Hall Assizes. Her uncle, leader of the American Confederates, pleaded for her life to be spared, and as a result Florence Maybrick was reprieved.

I have visited St George's Hall on numerous occasions, and have always experienced something different on each visit. Many people have reported shadowy forms in the bowels of the building where the cells can still be seen today. In the basement of St George's Hall lie rusting Sirens from World War Two, reminders of the part the building played during the war. A ghostly soldier has been seen wondering through the corridors, seemingly in a confused state, before disappearing into the shadows. Light anomalies have also been reported floating down the dark corridors of the basement, even though no lights were on at the time. There is very little doubt that St George's Hall is best visited at night and when the building is in total darkness.

One time as my friend and I made our way down the staircase leading from the dock to the cells below, we both heard whispering voices and felt as though someone was trying to push us aside. We lingered for a moment at the bottom of the stairs and could see the diminutive grey figure of a lady in a long dress. It's funny that they always seem to either be grey or white. Maybe these are the prerequisite colours for being a ghost!

St George's Hall has also attracted many unusual people, such as the two world-renowned American 'physical' mediums, Ira and William Davenport. They had caught the imagination of the world with their demonstrations of Spirit materialization, and other unusual phenomena, such as musical instruments being played by disembodied hands, whilst they themselves were securely tied up inside the obligatory materialization cabinet. The brothers had travelled all over the world, demonstrating their 'extraordinary' paranormal skills to capacity audiences, but their visit to St George's Hall in the mid 1860s, proved to be their downfall.

Victorian Spiritualists were frequently spellbound when selected members of the audience were invited to tie the brothers securely to their chairs. Once done, the curtain was drawn across the cabinet, and ectoplasm exuded from the cabinets, and took the shape of 'spirit hands' and other unusual disembodied forms. Musical instruments would also be seen playing as they floated through the air in front of the audience. However, on one particular night whilst appearing in Liverpool, the man they invited from the audience to secure them tightly with knots, was a suspicious dock worker from Merseyside. He and his friend bound the two mediums so securely with 'special' knots, that Ira and William Davenport found it impossible to struggle free. The charlatans' demonstration was thus thwarted and the audience's angry rage prevailed throughout the hall. They made a hasty retreat from St George's Hall with the Liverpool audience in angry pursuit. They had been duping audiences all over the world for many years, but got their comeuppance when they came to Liverpool. Before Ira died he confessed to Harry Houdini that he and his brother, William, had in fact been 'faking' it for years.

SUPERSTITIONS

From a very early age most of us have grown up with the beliefs and superstitions passed on to us by our parents. And even though we secretly know these to be just ill informed nonsense, they are so deeply embedded in our subconscious that we dare not disregard them for fear that something dreadful will befall us. Even today I simply will not walk under a ladder, just in case it brings me bad luck, or something terrible happens to me. Even though I have no idea where this belief came from, I will not, and cannot, take the chance. My mother would not do it, so I most certainly will not.

However, some omens and superstitions do make a great deal of sense and clearly do have more than a grain of truth in them.

For example, I grew up believing that you should never cut your toenails on a Sunday. This, I am quite convinced, was a superstition created by my mother in order to stop my father from performing such an unpleasant practice in the living room, just before Sunday lunch was served. Another superstition passed on from my mother, was to never play cards on a Sunday. If you do, my mother assured me that the devil would play with us also.

Other beliefs are so ridiculous that they are obviously designed to instil fear into the vulnerable and gullible. For example – never cross another person on the stairs! In the house where I lived as a child, this was not only ridiculous, but also an impossibility, for the stairs were so narrow that there was only enough room for one person at a time.

'See a pin, pick it up, and all the day you'll have good luck.' How ridiculous. My mother collected so many pins that there was very little room in her purse for any money.

I remember watching an elderly woman at the bus stop knowingly allowing her bus to go on without her, because she had dropped her glove on the pavement and wanted someone to pick it up for her.

Although I could never understand my mother saying, 'A knife to the floor and a man to the door,' she always seemed to be right. Every time she dropped a knife on the floor, a man would call at the house for one reason or another.

Some superstitions never really made any sense to me, and I could never see why crossed knives were unlucky. They do say that the crossed knives superstition originated with the crossed swords in a duel. The belief is that when knives cross on the table an argument ensues.

Another superstition is to never place new shoes on a table or flat surface. This portends a long period of bad luck, and in the grimmest scenario DEATH! The origins of this morbid superstition originate with 13 wooden steps up to the gallows.

As a child I used to laugh with delight as my father threw a pinch of salt over his left shoulder after spilling it on the table. This ancient superstition of spilling salt necessitated throwing the salt as an offering to the spirits. Even he was superstitious about some things.

I remember when my grandmother died and her coffin had been placed on trestles in the parlour, all the mirrors in the house were covered with a black cloth. This was to ensure that my grandmother's reflection could not be seen in the mirror.

Then there was the time I got smacked for accidentally breaking a mirror. 'We'll have bad luck for seven years now,' my mother said, with a worried look upon her face. Apparently, bad luck only follows a broken mirror if it is broken on purpose. That's all right then.

The superstition of touching wood to protect you when you have tempted fate in some way has a biblical origin. The followers of Jesus touched the wood of the cross as a mark of respect. Knocking on wood is also supposed to scare off evil spirits. Crossing fingers also has Christian connotations. Long before the cross was a Christian symbol of recognition, a drawing of a fish was used. Crossed fingers designated the fish and were used as a secret sign to let other Christians know you were a follower of Jesus.

One of the most ridiculous superstitions originated in the trenches in the First World War when a soldier was shot dead after taking the third light for his cigarette. I wonder what would have happened if he had been shot dead after the first one? Smoking would have then been a thing of the past.

What about the superstition about the number 13? It is unlucky to seat 13 people at a table, most probably because of the 13 people seated at the Last Supper. In ancient Babylon, 13 people were chosen to personify the god in a religious ceremony. However, one person was always seated away from the others, and he or she was the one chosen to be sacrificed. It is said that if there are 13 letters in your name you are cursed with the luck of the devil. Charles Manson, Theodore Bundy to name but two infamous characters with 13 letters in their names. Many people believe that if 13 people sit down to dinner, they will all die within one year. The ancient Hindus and Vikings believed that it was unlucky for 13 people to gather in one place. Infact, number 13 is very rarely seen in any street, and the 13th floor in any tall building is very often referred to as either the 113th floor, or the 14th floor. The number 13 is often associated with death, misfortune or even the devil.

I have always found the black cat superstition quite fascinating. For example, Winston Churchill was born on Friday 13th, and he would never pass a black cat without stroking it. Napoleon, however, had a dread of black cats. If he saw one he believed that bad luck would befall him. Some people believe that it is lucky for a black cat to cross your path, whilst others believe the opposite. All black cat superstitions are believed to originate from the fact that witches had their black familiars – the wise cats that always accompanied them.

Another silly superstition is about tripping on the stairs. Tripping up the stairs is said to mean a birth, tripping down the stairs portends death. This is one of those little known superstitions, but I suppose that now you know about it, many of you will take care not to do it – at least not to trip on your way down.

Then we have those portentous omens that are usually associated with death. Knocking sounds from within a cupboard, or ottoman, is one example of a portent of death. Clocks suddenly stopping, or falling off a wall or mantelpiece, and a mirror or picture suddenly falling from the wall are viewed similarly. A dog howling was nearly always considered to be an omen of misfortune or approaching bad news. When anyone dies a dog always howls. Have you ever noticed this?

The reflection of a new moon in a mirror would always necessitate the turning of silver coins in the pocket. Do this, and you would be guaranteed good fortune, ignore the omen, and misfortune would most certainly befall you. I could never understand why a purse could not be given as a gift without first of all placing a coin inside it. Or why a knife of any sort had be accompanied by a coin before given as a present. It would appear that, like dialects, which are peculiar to certain geographical locations, superstitions too vary somewhat from place to place.

As a child I would suddenly get it into my head that I could not walk on the cracks on the pavement. If I managed to follow my route all the way home without treading on any cracks, I was convinced that I would become a millionaire. I am not sure what happened, perhaps I walked on a crack without realising it!

I am quite certain that some superstitions are created by children who often possess the power to turn a simple phrase into a powerful incantation. 'Touch black, no back,' would have to be intoned to ensure that a transaction between playmates was fixed and the comics or toys could not be taken back after they had been swapped. As a child we would also have to put up with the annoying ritual of having our head touched and 'first wet,' called every time we had visited the barber.

Putting two different socks on by mistake was also meant to herald the approach of a lucky period, and wearing an item of clothing inside out was also supposed to be extremely lucky. If my mother inadvertently changed the month on a calendar before it was due, she would be certain that something untoward was going to happen to her. If a wild bird flew into the house, my mother would be adamant that someone was going to die, and if a gypsy woman called to the door, she would not send her away without purchasing a lucky charm, just in case she cursed her.

I suppose the majority of people from my mother's era were superstitious, and today the tradition has largely disappeared. Perhaps that is the problem in the so-called modern age of science and technology; there is only a small minority who have retained the tradition of adhering to superstitions. However, the majority of people 'touch wood' when tempting fate and 'never cast a clout till May is out!'

When walking along the pavement with your friend or partner, never let a lamppost or any other obstacle come between you. If you do your relationship will be broken.

When a question needs to be resolved and an answer is sought, a tossed coin frequently makes the decision. Some people feel that they have to wear a certain lucky tie, or even carry a particular lucky charm when going for an interview or into a situation in which extra luck is required.

Whenever I am going into a stressful situation, or perhaps appearing somewhere quite important, I always carry a photograph of Padre Pio. I also have to wear a certain pair of socks. Some people carry superstitions to the extreme and become obsessed to the point where it prevents them from doing something important. One man believed that rain was unlucky for him, and so missed an important interview because it was raining.

35

Genie in the Bottle and a Wish that Came True

Over the years I have collected thousands of stories, many of which are far too bizarre to be true. Nonetheless, I am frequently the captive audience for the storyteller eager to contribute to my growing collection of incredible paranormal tales. Although seemingly outside the bounds of possibility, I have included this story in the book primarily because it caught my interest and also because the person's wife confirmed that it did happen just as he had said. Also, the man who experienced this very unusual phenomenon was deeply affected as a direct consequence, and even to this day believes that he had been rewarded by a benevolent spirit simply because he unknowingly released it from an eternity of imprisonment. However, I will leave to you to decide.

Norman Joss always looked forward to the end of the summer, so that he could take his metal detector onto Southport Beach, with the hope of discovering lost pieces of jewellery, coins and anything else he could find buried in the sand. At the end of his two-hour mooch around on the beach, he always expected to take home a bucket full of miscellaneous items, and would be greatly disappointed if his find amounted to anything less than £30 or even £60 in lost money. Although his wife, Pat, usually accompanied him, she still thought he was crazy for doing what he did. After only half an hour, Norman usually had a pretty good idea whether or not the day was going to be productive, and always came prepared with a couple of cagoules, should it rain, two folding chairs and a flask of tea with an ample supply of sandwiches.

On this particular day there had been a little drizzle and the sand was quite damp. Norman had only just begun sweeping his metal detector across the surface of the sand when it started to oscillate loudly. Once he'd decided exactly where to dig, he began his usual process of gently disturbing the sand with his trowel, and no more than six inches below the surface, he located an old earthenware bottle, sealed with some sort of metal stopper, which the metal detector had located. Once he had extricated the bottle from the sand, he brushed his hand across it, clearing away as much of the grime as possible, and making the engraving on the top of the stopper more visible. It was some sort of symbol and obviously quite old. The bottle itself seemed to be more than a few hundred years old at least, and looked as though it had been sealed for just as long. Both Norman and his wife were curious about the contents of the bottle and, abandoning the dig, they returned to the car for a cup of tea and a sandwich. Although it took a great deal of force, Norman eventually broke the seal and pulled it free from the bottle. The couple were almost immediately overwhelmed by a strong fragrance oozing from the bottle, and a loud swishing sound followed almost immediately. He looked at his wife and shrugged, puzzled. He then shook the bottle onto a newspaper and was surprised to see an iridescent green powder fall onto it. Norman didn't know what to make of it, but decided almost immediately to scoop it back into the bottle anyway, before continuing with the dig.

That night they both woke up at exactly the same time, sometime around 3am. 'I had the most peculiar dream,' said Norman, swinging his legs over the side of the bed. 'You'll never believe it.'

'I would,' retorted his wife. 'Because I've just had a weird dream too.'

As it turned out Norman and his wife had had exactly the same dream, in which they saw an old, wise looking man holding the earthenware bottle in front of him. They both described the ghostly figure as being clad in the robes of an eastern guru. 'I could hear his voice clearly,' added Norman. 'He thanked me for releasing him from the bottle, and said it was the customary practise of his people to grant one wish in return for the good deed.'

As Norman was talking, his wife nodded in agreement, confirming that this was exactly what the man had said to her. 'Does this mean we are both granted a wish?'

'Will you listen to yourself,' scoffed Norman, tiredly climbing back into bed. 'What's wrong with you, woman? It was just a bloody dream, that's all! Let's not get carried away. It wasn't the Genie of the Magic Lamp, you know. It was just an old bottle!' Within moments Norman was fast asleep and snoring, but his wife sat up in bed thinking. Their daughter had lived in Australia for four years, and the couple had only been to see her once in all that time. Now that Norman had retired, they had to watch their pennies. 'It would be nice if...' Pat had fallen asleep.

When Pat checked her lottery ticket the following Saturday, she couldn't believe it when all their numbers had come up. She excitedly handed Norman the ticket to check, and he confirmed that they did indeed have all six numbers.

Although Norman and Pat would not disclose exactly how much they had won, it did change their lives in more ways than one. Although Pat never told her husband until much later, that she had secretly made a wish, just in case, she was certain that their lottery win had something to do with the old bottle. Incidentally, the bottle disappeared without trace, and was never seen again. Unless, of course, Norman had discarded it without telling his wife.

36

The Ghosts of Thurstaston

Having now lived in Lower Heswall for five years, I have come to realise that, although only a short distance across the River Mersey from Liverpool, it is a completely different world all together! Steeped in history, the ancient villages of Lower Heswall and Thurstaston appear to be somehow locked in time, and even the people here seem to belong to another age, in the nicest possible way, you understand.

Not far from Heswall is Thurstaston, allegedly named after a Viking farmer called Thorstein. The word 'Ton' is Viking for farm or settlement, and there is evidence everywhere in this picturesque place that the Vikings did settle here and even cultivated most of the surrounding land.

Standing in front of St Bartholomew's Church in Thurstaston Village, no real effort is required to transport yourself back to another time. Next to the ancient church stands Thurstaston Hall, reputed to date from 1070 A.D, and occupied by the same family for over 600 years. The hall itself possesses a sinister past, and was the location of the alleged murder of a young boy. Many so-called 'haunted houses' have a White Lady, and Thurstaston Hall is no exception. The perpetrator of the boy's demise is said to roam through the corridors of the old house, in search of the child she had murdered. The owners of the hall seem to regard the ghostly apparitions as no more than rumours, and were not able to confirm the ghostly stories connected to the old house. The owners of Thurstaston Hall refused to allow my wife and I to take a look at the alleged haunted rooms, and so we were therefore unable to experience the phenomena for ourselves.

Many ghostly sightings have been reported on the small green in front of the house and the church. A ghostly horse rider has been seen on numerous occasions, galloping through the village in the dead of night, eventually disappearing into the darkness. An elderly gentleman on a bicycle has also been seen, casually peddling his way along the road, before finally disappearing into the surrounding air.

I have visited Thurstaston Village in the dead of night and once saw a sequence of strange light anomalies moving quickly along the road in front of the church.

Some historians believe that the very name 'Thurstaston' originates from the Viking God Thor. This may also account for the name given to a large piece of sandstone called locally 'Thor's Stone', and linked directly to the God Thor. The ancient stone was also most probably a place of pagan worship, as well as a sacrificial alter. Locals say that the ancient stone is frequently struck by lightening, perhaps an indication of all the evil energy it has attracted during its lifetime.

Thurstaston beach is a beautiful place to picnic, if you don't mind descending the hundreds of steps to get to it, and an even more exhausting journey on the way back up.

It is at this point of the picturesque landscape that smugglers would unload their boats, occasionally being killed by customs officers when they put up a struggle. The beach is quite eerie at night, with disembodied voices echoing on the Estuary breeze. Shadowy forms can frequently be seen here without any great effort, and a group of ghostly Viking Warriors, with swords drawn, have been seen running from the water. Some people have claimed that they have seen a ghostly Viking boat, with masts high, floating spookily through Estuary mists. Since moving to Lower Heswall we have seen many strange and weird anomalies that I as a medium cannot explain.

Billy says: Apart from its historical interest, Lower Heswall and Thurstaston are well worth a visit. One of the reasons that there appears to be so much paranormal activity there, is that it seems to be situated on a network of ley lines, and this phenomenon appears to act as some sort of conduit, occasionally dissipating the incredible build-up of energy. In other words, it is just like walking through a cinema whilst the film is being projected on a very large screen. Although you can see the film, those taking part in the film are not aware of you. In saying that, I still would not take a walk there at night by myself. Just in case!

37

THE MYSTERY OF OLD MA' CLEGG

For me growing up in the fifties and sixties was an incredibly exciting time, as I'm sure it was for everyone my age. In the 1950s there were still visible signs of the war all over Liverpool, and amazingly some families simply refused to abandon their homes, even when they had been extensively damaged during the relentless air raids. Fortunately for me I was born after the Second World War, but as a young boy I could still see the damage Wavertree (where I lived) had sustained. There were bomb craters in every street, and the sad remains of houses stood as constant reminders of the pounding Liverpool had taken during the so-called 'Blitz'. Old Ma' Clegg was a familiar figure round the streets of Wavertree in the early 1950s; a tiny, frail woman whose age was very difficult to tell. Apart from her name nobody knew anything about Ma' Clegg, and my mother always said that that was the way she liked it. She would frequently be seen wandering the streets of Wavertree, occasionally turning down back entries to avoid the childrens' tormenting chants of 'Old Ma' Clegg is a dirty old witch! Old Ma' Clegg is a...'

Thinking back now I can see just how cruel children could and probably still can be, and I'm quite sure that this sprightly little lady did not deserve the constant torment and ridicule. Occasionally she would brave the groups of children playing on the corner, and would even give chase when they called her names. One boy told me that she had chased and caught his friend for calling after her, and that she had taken him captive in her home and he was never seen again. I'm quite sure now that that tale was not true, but it did make the whole idea of old Ma' Clegg being a witch more realistic.

Old Ma' Clegg lived by herself in a derelict house in Wavertree. Her tatty coat was tied around the middle with a piece of string, and she was frequently seen wearing two odd shoes. Although she was always dressed shabbily, she never looked dirty. On the contrary, her shoulder-length grey hair always looked shiny and very clean, and although she had become a recognised, eccentric figure on the streets of Wavertree, she always seemed to me to be carrying a huge cloud of sadness around with her. I once allowed my curiosity to lead me to investigate her house, and as I was peering through the grime on the window to see what was inside, she came out of the back door and nearly caught me. 'I'll have you in my pot,' she called, grinning through broken yellow teeth and shaking her fist at me. I was terrified, but at least I never went near Old Ma' Clegg's house ever again.

There was another side to Old Ma' Clegg; a side only adults knew about. Old Ma' Clegg was a herbalist and had treated many of the people in Wavertree during the war.

Since the age of three I had suffered with an incurable lung condition, and as a consequence was frequently hospitalised for treatment. As antibiotics were comparatively new, apart from penicillin there were very few others on the market. I had been laid up in bed with a chest infection, and a course of penicillin had seemingly not had any effect. My mother popped her head in my bedroom. 'Won't be long,' she smiled. 'Just nipping on a message.' She had been gone no longer than 20 minutes when she returned. 'Brought somebody to see you.' She walked into the bedroom followed by, of all people, Old Ma' Clegg!

I felt my whole body stiffen with fear as the old woman stood at the side of my bed, eyeing me curiously, her thin lips parted into a slight smile, sufficiently for me to see her badly stained teeth. I grimaced as she leaned over to place her hand on my forehead, nodding and mumbling to herself once she had made her final diagnosis. I breathed a huge sigh of relief as she left the bedroom, and a few moments later I heard the front door downstairs close. My mother stood by the side of the bed with her arms folded, grinning at me. She knew what had been going through my mind, and could also see the look of sheer terror in my eyes. A further 20 minutes went by and the old woman was back in my room, clutching a brown medicine bottle. My mother gave Ma' Clegg a tablespoon and she immediately proceeded to pour the deep red liquid onto it, before forcing it into my mouth. I was surprised that Ma' Glegg's concoction tasted quite pleasant, and so I did not mind when she shoved another spoonful between my lips. Before leaving, the old woman gave my mother instructions on how and when to administer her magical potion. 'I would normally charge sixpence for this, but on this occasion there's no charge.' She left without saying goodbye, and I fell almost immediately into a deep sleep. Thanks to Old Ma' Clegg and her concoction, I recovered from the severe infection without further antibiotics. I later learned from my mother that the dark red liquid was a very special blend of beetroot juice, vinegar, honey and a very secret ingredient, known only to Old Ma' Glegg! When my friends found out what had happened they teased me and said that her secret ingredient was a blend of rat poo and wee mixed in with crushed cockroaches. Children can be so cruel, can't they?

Billy says: I'm not sure whether Old Ma' Clegg died or whether she was placed in a rest home for the elderly, as my mother had said. She just disappeared completely and her house was demolished.

38

The Mystery of George Germain Foney

During the reign of George III, when the slave trade was still considered a very acceptable and lucrative business, an advertisement appeared in Williamson's Advertiser, informing readers of a 'Runaway slave', and offering a handsome reward for his capture. The man in question was George Germain Foney, slave to Captain Ralph, a well-known and respected figure in the area of Prescot, from where Foney had escaped. The runaway slave was described as 'rather handsome, well dressed, and speaks English fairly well.' The majority of those who read the weekly newspaper were more interested in capturing Foney for the reward than they were simply for his safe return to Captain Ralph. As the wealthy captain was thought to be a kind and gentle man, the majority of people living in Prescot could not understand why George Germain Foney could even think of running away, let alone actually doing so. An extensive search was conducted for the slave, who had, to all intents and purposes, disappeared off the face of the earth. Rumours began to circulate that the escaped slave had taken refuge in a nearby monastery, but when the authorities searched the premises this was proved to be wrong. As there were some captains who openly opposed slave trafficking, there were even suggestions that Foney had escaped on a ship from Liverpool and returned to his home in Africa. However, as the authorities were very vigilant in and around the dock areas of Liverpool, this was dismissed as being impossible. Although many slaves attempted to escape, they were usually quickly caught and punished. However, George Germain Foley somehow managed to avoid being recaptured, giving hope to others that escape from slavery was possible. Foley somehow caught the imagination of the people of Liverpool, and became an inspiration to all black slaves.

What happened to George Germain Foley still remains a mystery even to this day. According to records, he would have been 47 when slave trading was finally abolished in 1807, and the last slave ship sailed out of Liverpool. One of the last ships to leave Liverpool was the Mary, captained by Hugh Crowe, believed to have been one of the kindest men for the way in which he treated the slaves he carried.

39

The Ghosts of the Bluecoat

In School Lane, a road that runs from Hanover Street, parallel to Church Street, stands the architecturally impressive Bluecoat, first opened in the reign of George 1, sometime in 1708. Originally intended as a school for deprived children, founded by Robert Stithe, a clergyman, and Bryan Blundell a sea captain. Both men shared a love of children, and the overwhelming desire to do all in their power to help with their education.

Records show that their first building cost the meagre sum of £35 to build, and this accommodated 50 children. They employed one headmaster, giving him the princely sum of £20 a year. Although Robert Stithe and Bryan Blundell were extremely passionate about their school, they were badly in need of funds to enable them to continue with their good work. Leaving Stithe in charge of things, Blundell returned to sea, with the sole intention of securing more capital for their benevolent project. In 1713, five years later, Stithe died, leaving Blundell in a huge emotional dilemma. He had to decide which was more important to him, the school or the sea. Blundell knew only too well that if he returned to sea the school would have to close. The decision was easily made and he gave up going away to sea and remained at the school to continue the work he loved so much.

Although the school eventually moved to Church Road in Wavertree, in 1906, the ghosts of the past remained in the original building. As well as the sound of childrens' disembodied playful laughter, echoing through the corridors of the Bluecoat, a ghostly hurdy-gurdy has been heard to the accompanying sound of children singing. Shadowy forms are also frequently seen wandering through the draughty corridors, and it is thought that the ghosts of Robert Stithe and Bryan Blundell are still there, looking after the school that they both founded and loved so much.

Over the years, visitors to the Bluecoat have reported seeing a man wearing a three cornered hat, peering down through an upstairs window. Could this be the ghost of Bryan Blundell or perhaps Robert Stithe? Who knows?

Although the whole area has been transformed, and the Bluecoat now completely refurbished, I am quite sure that the old school's ghostly inhabitants still see the place as it was when they lived there, and not as it is today. The Bluecoat will not give up its ghosts without a fight, even though time has moved on, the man wearing the three-cornered hat remains seated at the window.

40

The Ghosts of Leasowe Castle

Since being the home to the Earl of Derby's family, Leasowe Castle has changed hands several times over the years. It was built in 1593 for the fifth Earl of Derby, and was used primarily as his holiday home. At one time it was in the hands of an unstable man who bore a grievance with his neighbours. He was filled with so much hate for them, he took a father and his son prisoner and, until he decided their fate, kept them both locked up in a panelled room somewhere in the old castle. To avoid being murdered by the man, the father suffocated his son before battering his own brains out on the wall. The panelled room was awash with blood, and the owner of Leasowe Castle was charged with their demise.

A few hundred years later, the castle was converted into a hotel, and guests immediately complained to the management about spine-chilling, cries for help in the middle of the night, and the ghostly figures of the man and his son walking across the room. The hotel eventually fell into disrepair and closed down, but was then reopened sometime later as a Railwayman's Convalescent Home. However, today it is a hotel once again, and although there have been few reports of the ghostly activity, it is believed that the Earl of Derby Suite is the most haunted. Over the years numerous paranormal phenomena have been reported, and guests in the hotel have caught distorted ghostly images on film. Even if you

don't believe in ghosts and things that go bump in the night, it is still worth staying at Leasowe Castle. Go on, I dare you!

41

THE DEVIL IN BOOTLE

Although I have written about Teresa Helena Higginson in a previous chapter, I think her alleged encounters with the devil when she lived in Bootle need to be looked at more extensively.

The diminutive Teresa was nothing out of the ordinary to look at. She was nearly always shabbily dressed, but was quite refined and, had a gentleness that endeared her to everyone. It was quite obvious to those who knew her well that she was different. Although most people could see this, no one could quite put their finger on what it was about Teresa that made her different – she just was. She had a way with children, and it was this that led her into the teaching profession.

Life for the residents of Ariel Street, a quiet cul-de-sac in Bootle, changed dramatically, when Teresa Helena Higginson went to live at number 15 towards the end of the 20th century. She had taken up her new post as mistress at St Alexander's Elementary School, and moved into lodgings with other teachers at Ariel Street. She was well liked by the other tenants in the house, and befriended by Susan Ryland, who shared a room with her. At first, life for the young teachers was fairly quiet at the terrace house, until a commotion could be heard coming from Teresa's room late at night. Her friend, Susan Ryland, would frequently run anxiously from the room, calling for the other women to come and help. Teresa's room would often be seen in a state of disarray, and furniture and other objects would seemingly be thrown about the room by some unseen force. During this commotion Teresa would be in a trance-like state, and would remain so until everything had quietened down. The word quickly spread through Bootle that the Devil frequently called at 15 Ariel Street, and the diminutive Teresa Helena Higginson would always fight him off. Teresa confided in Reverend Canon Alfred Snow who was considered to be a man of high intelligence and integrity. He was heard to say that in his opinion Teresa was not only a saint, but also one of the highest saints.

Miss Minnie Catterall and her sister, occupied the room next door to Teresa, and were frequently woken in the middle of the night by loud noises. One night when Miss Catterall and her sister had just extinguished the lights and were about to retire, there was an extremely loud sequence of bangs coming from the room next door. These were followed by the most horrific wailing sound, almost like a banshee. The commotion continued into the night. The same thing happened the following night. However, Miss Catterall and her sister were more concerned that nobody else in the house had heard the unearthly sounds. The handle of the Catterall sisters' bedroom door would rattle, and they would hear the most fiendish laugh, followed by screaming coming from Teresa's bedroom. On one particular night, the sisters ventured out onto the landing, and they claimed that the most horrific man with bulging, demonic eyes confronted them. They said that he extended his very long tongue and hissed at them. They were so terrified they ran back into the room and locked the door. Although everyone living at 15 Ariel Street made every attempt to suppress the rumours that the devil frequently visited Teresa Helena Higginson, she soon became the talk of the neighbourhood, and was revered as a holy woman who fought the devil. Of course, as is always the case with people such as Teresa Helena Higginson, the cynics accused her of drunkenness and fabrication. Teresa shrugged off these suggestions and continued living her life in the best way she could. Although she died in 1905, today she is still referred to as the woman who fought and beat the devil in Bootle. One interesting thing about Teresa Helena Higginson is the way she affected those who were close to her. Her good friend, Susan Ryland, with whom she shared her most secret thoughts, became a nun, and spent the rest of her life in a convent. Also, the nurse who looked after Teresa up until the day she died, became a Poor Clare in one of the strictest, religious orders for women. Even though the sceptics went on criticising Teresa after her death, thousands of people speak of her with respect and reverence, and those all over the world who, to this day, still regard her as a saint venerate her memory.

42

The Ghosts of the Balmoral Suite

Many famous and interesting people have stayed at the Prince of Wales Hotel in Southport. Set back on busy Lord Street, the fine hotel quietly reposes amidst the hustle and bustle of an ever-changing seaside resort. The Balmoral Suite has, like the rest of the hotel, seen much better days, and is badly in need of refurbishment. Nonetheless, loyal holidaymakers still adhere to their yearly ritual of staying at the hotel, unaware that they are probably partaking of their afternoon tea in the company of the hotel's ghostly residents of the past. Because of circumstances beyond our control, my wife, Dolly and I (although we were not married then) had cause to stay in the Balmoral suite for four months. The first couple of weeks were really just like being on holiday, but then it began to feel more like a punishment than a joy. Personal effects would seemingly just disappear, only to turn up again, days later, in a completely different place. We frequently saw the ghostly figures of an Edwardian man and woman casually walking across the room, eventually disappearing through the closed door. We were woken on many occasions by someone jumping on the end of the bed, and other times the bed covers would all be pulled off the bed and thrown onto the floor. Although the acoustics in the hotel were quite unusual, and it was normal to hear sounds drifting up from the hotel lobby below, we frequently heard our names being called from the adjacent room, and when we went to investigate there was never anybody there.

As a medium I am not expected to be frightened, however I would rarely sleep with the light off!

Although in the past I have stayed in other rooms in the Prince of Wales, I have never experienced anything as we did in the Balmoral Suite. I have never made any enquiries about the history of the suite, and thought I would sooner remain ignorant about its ghostly past, just in case I did not like what I was told. I can only say that there were all different sorts of paranormal phenomena in the Balmoral Suite, and I have no doubt whatsoever that it is quite haunted. I have spoken to an American couple who once stayed in the suit for two weeks, and they also experienced some 'strange and spooky goings on in.'

'Would you stay there again?' I asked them.

'Absolutely,' came their immediate reply. 'We love anything to do with English ghosts!' There was absolutely nothing I could say to that was there?

43

Spring Heeled Jack - Fact or Fiction

The legend of an immensely agile demonic-looking figure, frequently seen during Victorian times, has no doubt been exaggerated over the years. Numerous writers have exploited the concept of Spring Heeled Jack to the full, and have created frightening tales of a cloaked figure sprinting over rooftops and high buildings to escape being caught. In fact, the concept of such a demonic figure has given rise to many theoretic opinions, most of which are pure supposition and conjecture. Spring Heeled Jack was allegedly seen in different parts of Victorian England, and was said to be very tall, cloaked in black with bulging red eyes, with flames streaming from his mouth. He was also said to be able to leap incredible heights over the highest buildings. Some journalists wrote that in their opinion Spring Heeled Jack was a deranged circus acrobat who simply delighted in causing mayhem and frightening people. Although there are no records of him having ever really hurt anyone, many claimed to have been confronted by the sprightly demonic, hideous looking figure. Despite the fact that records show his last sighting was in Liverpool in 1904, my grandmother always claimed that she was one of a crowd of 20 people who watched Spring Heeled Jack leap from Walton Road onto the roof of the Astoria Picture house. This apparently took place sometime in the winter of 1918, when my mother was four, and a time when several sightings were reported of Spring Heeled Jack in Liverpool. Although my grandmother unfortunately died six months before I was actually born, my mother always affirmed that she was a robust, down-to-earth woman who was never given to flights of fancy. As my mother was also that way inclined, I really had no cause to doubt her. In fact, my mother also told me that my grandmother was one of those interviewed about the sighting, and that it was something she never, ever forgot.

Although many of Spring Heeled Jack's descriptions contradict each other, the one thing they all have in common is his extremely surreal physiognomy. This included clawed hands and fiery red eyes, an elongated face with hideous and yet very frightening features. To all intents and purposes, Spring Heeled Jack had a devil-like appearance, and many witnesses said that he could breathe red and white flames. Early witnesses of this demonic figure claimed that he spoke extremely good English. Unfortunately, because of Spring Heeled Jack's many and varied bizarre description's his whole image was taken up by many writers of fiction at that time. The story of this Victorian monster was most probably blown out of all proportion and, as a result of the general public's perception of Spring Heeled jack, so the myth of the demon was perpetuated.

One of the most fascinating stories of him took place with a young girl by the name of Mary Stevens, who was making her way to work in Lavender Hill after visiting her parents in Battersea. It was on her way through Clapham Common that she encountered the malevolent looking creature, who leapt on her from behind. According to the statement the young girl later gave the police, he clawed at her body and made every effort to rip off her clothes. She screamed and managed to struggle free, causing Spring Heeled Jack to sprint off in the opposite direction. The following day, the sprightly, leaping figure of Spring Heeled Jack, jumped in front of a passing carriage, causing the coachman to fall and injure himself. The incident was witnessed by several people who all said that the frightening figure of the leaping devil, jumped with great ease over a nine-foot fence to escape, laughing fiendishly as he did so.

As the descriptions of Spring Healed Jack were so varied over the years, the question still remains, was he fact or fiction? Or, as one notable writer suggested, perhaps there were in fact more than one Spring Healed Jack! After all, he was seen from one end of Britain to the other, and sometimes simultaneously. What do you think?

44

Destination Unknown

No matter how strong we think we are, nothing can ever prepare us for the death of someone we love. Bereavement is perhaps one of the most difficult emotional pains with which we have to cope during our lives, and we never known when it is going to strike. June Parry was devastated when Richie, her husband, died at the relatively young age of 53. He had been her constant companion since she was 17, and now she was all alone. Her only son was working in America, and although he came home as often as his work allowed, she still felt sad and lonely.

Richie had been a computer enthusiast, and had also fancied himself as a writer. He knew he was not talented enough to be a successful author, but this did not deter him in any way whatsoever. He had enjoyed writing so much that he would sometimes stay up until the early hours of the morning, lost in his own little world of fantasy and fiction. Now June was left alone with her memories and the remains of her husband's dreams and aspirations.

Although June was quite religious and attended church regularly every Sunday, Richie was a life-long agnostic and always joked that people who went to church were simply hedging their bets, or playing safe, 'just in case'.

'Well,' June always protested to her husband, 'where do you think we all go to when we die?'

'Destination unknown, Captain Kirk,' he would always answer

sarcastically. 'Destination unknown!'

Richie had been dead for six months now and June was sitting quietly in front of the computer, composing an e-mail to her son in America. Suddenly her husband came into her mind and her thoughts began to wander away from what she was doing. She found herself thinking about all the good times she and Richie had enjoyed together, and was suddenly utterly overwhelmed with grief and loss.

A few minutes elapsed and June eventually collected her thoughts and composed herself sufficiently to continue writing the email to her son. After a few more sentences she paused for a moment and stared sadly at the screen, her thoughts turning to her dead husband once more. She wondered what most people in her position think, 'Where is Richie now?' And almost in that moment, June noticed that someone had sent her an email message. She naturally assumed that it was from her son and immediately clicked the box to read her message.

It simply read: 'DESTINATION UNKNOWN – I LOVE YOU.'

No one but June had known what Richie used to say, and now she knew that he was fine – wherever he was.

45

The Ghosts of the Mystery

Wavertree Playground, or the 'Mystery' as it is known locally, is deeply engrained in the consciousness of every person who has grown up around it over the years. It has become an institution to the people of Wavertree, and even in my own childhood during the 1950s, many happy hours were spent in the Mystery. I mentioned in one of my earlier books that many people had reported seeing ghostly German soldiers, prisoners of war, who had been interned in the park during the Second World War. However, it would seem that other ghostly figures have been seen over the years, such as the ghost of Max, an elderly man who used to spend most of his days sitting on a bench in the park, just watching life pass him by. Old Max had lived by himself since his wife had died just after the war, and so with very little else to do, the park was his only enjoyment. Max's ghostly figure is sometimes seen with his dog, a wire-haired mongrel that would always accompany him during his daily sojourns in the Mystery.

GHOSTLY FORMS

Many years before a sports complex was built in the grounds of the Mystery, it was a pleasure to casually stroll through it on a warm summer's day, feeling the fresh afternoon breeze against your face, and watching the lush, green grass blowing evenly all across the park. In the 1950s and 60s all that could be found in the

Mystery .were the children's swings situated by the Wellington Road entrance, and a dilapidated cricket pavilion somewhere in the middle of the park. There were benches strategically situated here and there, and several Victorian black iron drinking fountains could occasionally be found along your path, enabling you to quench your thirst on a particularly warm day. At sunset the park attendant would cycle from one gate to the other, ensuring that the park was empty, before finally locking the large iron gates for the night. As a child I always wondered whether it was his intention to lock people out of the park, or mischievously lock people in. When I was about nine years old, my friend, Cliffy Jones, persuaded me to hide in the park until the gates had been locked, and then to walk through the darkness from one side to the other, just to see if it was really haunted. Having been psychic since I was a child, it was probably easier for me to 'see' ghostly images than it was for him. Nonetheless, I still found it all very exciting and had no idea what demons or ghostly figures we would encounter along our path. There had been several murders and some suicides in the park over the years, and I did wonder if the ghosts of these people would still be there. As Cliffy and I made our way bravely through the darkness, the deeper we entered into the park, the quicker our steps seemed to move. Once in the centre of the park we both realised that there was absolutely no turning back. We held on tightly to each other and ran as fast as we could, each step taking us deeper into the darkness, with no moon or stars to lighten our way. Suddenly my friend stopped, and pointed to something ahead. There were two glowing figures floating slowly towards us, their pulsating forms spookily moving above the surface of the ground. Although Cliffy was never fazed by anything, I knew that he too was terrified. Our attention was caught by other ghostly forms, shadowy figures moving through the darkness. Our feet seemed to find a new lease of life, and we fled as fast as our legs could carry us, not stopping until we had reached our nearest point of escape, over the railings in the side street leading on to nearby High Street.

When I told my mother what we had done, she laughed. 'Many

people have seen the phantoms of the Mystery,' she told me. 'The park is haunted.'

Over the years many people have recounted their experiences of the ghostly glowing forms in the Mystery in the dead of night. One scientific theory is that they are not the ghosts of the so-called 'dead', but images of people still very much alive in their own time – somewhere in the past. Could it be then that the past, the present and the future, exist simultaneously side by side? Perhaps nobody ever really dies. Maybe we simply move from the present to the future, or even to the past.

Billy says: I have no doubt whatsoever, that the Mystery is an extremely haunted park. Over the years many strange things have been seen there; things that simply cannot be explained.

46

The Mystery of Kitty Wilkinson

Most people in Liverpool are familiar with the name Kitty Wilkinson, and are most probably aware also of the good work she did with the impoverished in Liverpool during the reign of Queen Victoria. Even though today there are people who struggle to make ends meet, poverty in this day and age is nowhere near what it was during the days when Kitty Wilkinson gave her time to help those in need. In 1837 Liverpool was so overcrowded that it earned the reputation of being the unhealthiest town in the whole of England. It was thought to be so unhealthy to live in Liverpool that it was branded with the name of the 'black spot on the Mersey', a title that brought shame to all its inhabitants. In 1837 Liverpool had 220,000 people living there, and this amount doubled in just 34 years. The conditions in which people were forced to live, were in fact so overcrowded, that the mortality rate rapidly grew, and those who were fortunate enough to survive, suffered poor health as a consequence.

One wonders what made someone like Kitty forfeit what little she had to help the sick and the needy. She was born in Londonderry and brought to Liverpool with her baby sister by her widowed mother. The ship upon which they were travelling sustained extensive damage during a violent storm, and the crew and passengers were forced to abandon the vessel before it was pulled by turbulence to the bottom of the sea. Although both Kitty and her mother survived, Kitty's baby sister was carried away by a powerful wave that struck their small boat. The infant's death deeply affected her mother, whose mental health slowly deteriorated as a consequence. Kitty worked quite happily for seven years in a cotton mill near Lancaster, and only returned to Liverpool to look after her sick mother. She took a job in a Liverpool nail factory, and was paid the meagre sum of three pennies for making 1,200 nails. She earned approximately four shillings a week, and on some occasions her take home pay would be as much as eight shillings. Handling the hot materials from which the nails were made caused her fingers to become badly festered. As a result Kitty was forced to give up the job and was out of work until her hands had fully healed. She and her mother then set up their own little business making lace caps, and Kitty would go out on the streets and sell them. Kitty was not afraid of hard work, and did what ever she could to survive. She was deeply affected by the poverty stricken inhabitants of Liverpool, and although she herself had very little in the way of money, she was only too aware that there were others far worse off. The door of her own home in Denison Street was ever open to anyone in need. Although Kitty sought no reward for helping the needy, news of her good work quickly spread. She was frequently heard saying 'Nobody was any the poorer for what they gave to a neighbour in distress.' And although her own life was a struggle, she did all that she could possibly do to help those in need. One of her sons sadly died of consumption, and another was seen to be wild and unruly, and often brought shame to his mother. He went to the Bluecoat school, and never showed any gratitude to anyone for the way he himself had been helped.

Kitty Wilkinson would often take a family of 14 into her own home, and would think nothing of feeding and clothing them out of her own pocket. During the great cholera outbreak in Liverpool in 1832, Kitty was seen working tirelessly caring for the sick and dying. She supplied blankets to keep those affected by the disease warm and comfortable, and helped to wash and disinfect the bedding and clothes of those who had been stricken by the disease in a boiler in her own kitchen. In fact, it was this that gave

Kitty the idea for the opening of the public wash-house, for which she eventually became famous. Her good work was relentless, and this hard working woman received help from many people, such as her good friends, Mr and Mrs William Rathbone whom, it is believed, made the people of Liverpool aware of the good work Kitty was doing. However, Kitty's best and closest friend was her husband, who supported her in everything she did.

In 1832, 14 years after the outbreak of cholera in Liverpool, the very first public baths and wash house was opened in Frederick Street, and Kitty and her husband were so proud to be placed in charge of it

Not long after the couple's good work was acknowledged by Queen Victoria, who presented them with an engraved silver tea service set, Kitty's loving husband died. Regardless of her great and very sad loss, she continued her good work with her son for a further four years, after which she made the towels to be used in the washing baths. Records show that she received 12 shillings for doing this job, which she continued right up until the day she died at the age of 73. Her body was laid to rest in St James' Cemetery, and even today her tomb is a reminder to us all how very different our lives might have been today, had it not been for someone like Kitty Wilkinson, a lady who cared.

Many people have claimed to have seen the ghostly diminutive form of Kitty, strolling casually through St James' Cemetery. What I can't understand is why this lady would choose the cemetery in which to be seen? Why not in any of the places in which she was seen to do her good work? I'm not too certain about this, are you?

Billy says: Surely, if anyone should be beatified, Kitty Wilkinson should be. Why hasn't she been honoured for the good work she did amongst the poor people of Liverpool? Maybe one day she will.

47

Oldfield Farm Revisited

The proprietors of Oldfield Farm in Lower Heswall, Wirral, are far too matter-of-fact and down-to-earth to be bothered about the ghostly goings on at their farm. Either that, or they have lived with their unseen guests for so long that they simply don't 'see' them as ghostly intruders at all. Mary Johnson was born and bred on Oldfield Farm and, today this is run extremely efficiently by her husband Peter and her son Sam. There has apparently been a dwelling house on the farm since the 12th century, and although today it is very different to how it was all those centuries ago, the old farmhouse still retains the magic and charm that was created by Mary's mother and father (now deceased), long before she herself was born. Apart from ghostly monks roaming across the farm in the dead of night, Mary's two elderly aunts have their own stories of historical figures who had once dined at the family table. Admiral Lord Nelson is believed to have eaten at the old farmhouse, before going off to fight at the Battle of Trafalgar. In fact, Mary recounts the stories quite nonchalantly of many well-known figures visiting the old farm hundreds of years ago. After reading the story about the tall ghostly monks in my first Spooky Liverpool book, she quietly admitted that, whilst half-asleep one night, she glimpsed them walking through her bedroom wall. Apart from all the farm's paranormal history, Oldfield Farm possesses a certain kind of charm that most certainly belongs to another age.

48

The Ghostly Lady and the Little Girl

Although now mostly flats, the fine Victorian houses overlooking directly onto Sefton Park, still retain their architectural beauty, that once made the whole leafy suburban area a much sought after place for the wealthy to live. In fact, it requires very little imagination to see how it once was when the families of merchants, barristers and sea captains inhabited the old houses, perhaps in an age when the huge divide between the wealthy and the poor was almost impossible to surmount.

In the spring of 1968, property developer Ian Harper bought one of the old houses overlooking the park in an auction. Although it was greatly in need of refurbishment, he had decided from the very moment the auctioneer's hammer went down, that he was going to live there, and not sell it on as his business colleagues had thought. Even as a child growing up in the 1940s he had always dreamed of living in one of the large houses overlooking Sefton Park, and vowed that one day he would do just that. Now his childhood dream had come true, and happily his parents were both still alive to enjoy it with him. Ian was married with an eight-year-old daughter, Christina, and Ian's wife Joanne shared his enthusiasm for the property he had bought, making it even more enjoyable. It was an ideal setting to bring up a family, and the couple had already decided that they could now think about having more children.

The property took precisely four months to finish, and they had now been living there for over two weeks, when Christina began talking about the nice lady with long white hair.

'What lady?' asked Joanne. 'There's nobody else living here.'

'The lady in the kitchen,' came the innocent reply. 'She said she lives here too.'

Even though Joanne dismissed her daughter's story as being imaginary she couldn't help feeling an icy chill pass through her. When she told Ian he just laughed. 'All children have imaginary friends. It sometimes helps them to cope with new or strange situations. When she settles down, her friend will disappear.'

'And so speaks Carl Jung,' she joked, shaking her head.

Christina mentioned the lady with long white hair several times after that, and Ian and Joanne had no option but to take their daughter seriously. 'Keep an eye on her,' Ian suggested, concerned that his daughter might have an emotional problem of some kind, perhaps due to the move. It wasn't until Joanne heard Christina talking to someone in the kitchen, that she realised that there might be something more to the lady with long white hair. Although the conversation was one-sided, Joanna snuck quietly into the kitchen. She couldn't believe her eyes when she saw an elderly lady with long white hair, standing by the sink and smiling at Christina. As soon as Joanna walked into the kitchen, the old lady disappeared right in front of her. Joanna froze to the spot, amazed that her daughter had been telling the truth all the time. At first Ian didn't believe his wife, and just laughed dismissively. 'I saw her with my own eyes,' she insisted. 'She disappeared right in front of me.

Although the couple knew that the ghostly lady obviously meant their daughter no harm, they took the decision to move.

'It's a pity,' said Ian. 'I've always wanted a house like this.'

'Me too,' agreed Joanne, 'but I'm not sharing my own with any ghost.'

They had no problem selling the house, and within four months they had settled into their new home, further down the road.

Some weeks later as Ian was driving down Sefton Park Drive, he noticed a police van and several police cars outside of the house they had sold. He later learned that the new owners had decided to turn the cellars into a studio of some kind (a part of the house Ian had not refurbished) and the remains of a decaying corpse had been discovered. The body they found they said was an old lady with long white hair. It was concluded that she had died of natural causes, quite some years ago.

49

The Little Boy Who Saw True

In 1910 Marjory Lloyd became concerned for her six-year-old son's psychological well being, when he suddenly began saying things one would not expect an adult to say, let alone a little boy. He began relaying messages from Marjory's 'dead' father (whom her young son, Edward, had never known) and would also frequently offer detailed descriptions of the way certain streets in Liverpool looked many, many years before he himself had been born. He could just about read, and did not excel at any particular subject at his school, St Lukes. In fact, Edward was way behind the other children in his class, and was considered by his teacher, Miss Daniels, to be somewhat of a dreamer. Nonetheless, he was an unusual little boy who possessed the ability to 'see' things nobody else could see. His mother, Marjory, never considered for one single moment that her son had been endowed with supernatural powers, as suggested by her friend, Maggie McNamara. Young Edward appeared simply to 'know' things about people, and whenever he felt something very strongly, he would think nothing of just blurting it out. His extraordinary abilities gradually alienated him from the other children in his school, and it was only then that the headmistress showed her concern, and suggested his mother should seek professional help.

Edward made some frightening prophecies about a World War, and even said that this war would start as a result of an assassination. The little boy was quite specific with everything he said, and always gave a detailed description of exactly how he thought things would happen. Even his own parents were quite unnerved by some of the things their son came out with, and rumours began to circulate that he had 'special' powers. The neighbours in Sands Street where they lived were so fascinated by Edward's revelations that they were forever calling to their little terrace house to see if he could help resolve one problem or another. It was at this point that Edward's plight caught the interest of a local clergyman. 'A Russian scientist has been studying children with unusual powers,' he told his parents, 'and he is coming to Liverpool next month.'

Although Victorian England was becoming increasingly fascinated by the comparatively new religion, Spiritualism, it was still regarded by many as 'dabbling' with the unknown. Mediums were regarded as extremely unusual individuals, and although the majority of those who knew Edward were reluctant to label him with the name of 'medium', it was becoming increasingly obvious to everyone that that's exactly what he was. Although today Edward Lloyd's story would be quite acceptable, in Victorian England abilities of this nature were not openly spoken of. In any case, a child with such special abilities was very often regarded as 'odd' or at worse, 'marked by the devil'.

In 1903, Russian scientist, Professor Tutinsky, jeopardised his professional reputation, by making a detailed study of children with unusual abilities. Although Tutinsky took pains to avoid labels such as 'psychic' or 'paranormal', he did publicly acknowledge that such abilities were outside the parameters of tradition scientific thought, and therefore could not be measured in a laboratory. Although his peers ridiculed him for devoting so much of his time to the subject, he eventually concluded that, in his opinion the pineal gland, the walnut-shaped gland situated deep within the brain, was responsible for most, if not all, unusual activity exhibited by the human psyche. Tutinsky maintained that the pineal gland in the brain of a child is much larger than in the brain of an adult, and marginally more developed in a female than in the brain of a male. He went on to say, 'The majority of children grow out of such abilities; but for the minority in whom such unusual skills remain, an exciting and new dimension of possibilities unfold.'

Six-year-old Edward Lloyd's extra-sensory powers were a prime example, Tutinsky concluded. 'However, at this point there is no way of telling whether or not the boy will grow out of it.'

Edward Lloyd did not grow out of his unusual abilities, and in fact used his psychic skills up until the day he died in 1970 at the young age of 67.

Billy says: Many mediums have had their mediumistic skills since they were children. My own abilities became apparent around the age of three, and sometime around the age of 10 I was sent to see a child psychologist. The kind doctor concluded that I was sensitive, creative, and temperamental and possessed a vivid imagination. She was correct in her diagnosis. However, her prognosis that I would grow out of it was completely wrong - I did not!

50

THE UNINVITED LODGER

A few doors along Parliament Street, not far from where the Rialto Ballroom and cinema once stood, there was a grand old house, which was for many years, the home to an uninvited lodger – a ghost who simply refused to leave. It was 1947 and Liverpool was still recovering from the war. Jimmy and Vera Rice had been bombed out of their house in nearby Warwick Street, and had moved into a spacious, but dilapidated house in Parliament Street. This house too had sustained some damage during the Blitz, and had been empty since the last year of the war. Jimmy was a builder and Vera was used to turning her hand to almost anything, and so the couple were ready to restore the old house to its former glory. Besides that, they had two energetic teenage boys who could use a paintbrush at least.

As the roof was in need of extensive repair, the attic and two of the bedrooms were somewhat exposed to the elements, and so the family confined themselves to the rooms that were habitable. Jimmy wasted no time in repairing the roof, and two of his work colleagues helped with the plastering and decorating of the rooms.

They'd been living in the old house for just over three weeks and were sitting in the living room listening to the wireless, when they heard footsteps in the room directly above the one they were in. The boys were staying at their friends for the night, and so they knew there was no one else in the house. Jimmy and his wife went upstairs to investigate, but the rooms were empty. Vera held on tightly to her husband's hand as he moved bravely from one room to the other. He wasn't afraid of anything, but Vera could feel a cold shiver pass through her and felt as though someone was watching their every move. Once in the attic room, their footsteps echoed across the bare floorboards, and Jimmy looked at his wife and grinned. 'Told you. Nobody here. Old houses do make some funny noises.' He led his wife from the room and together they made their way downstairs. They had no sooner reached the hallway when they heard the ghostly footsteps once again. This time they distinctly heard a man laughing. Jimmy ran as quickly as he could back up the stairs, checking each room on his way – but, again there was nobody there. This time though, Vera could see that even her husband was a little freaked.

They both agreed that they would not tell the boys what had happened, and just hoped that there would not be a repetition of the disembodied sounds, especially at night when they were all in bed. However, their greatest fear happened, and continued to happen every night for the following week. Vera and the boys were petrified, and even Jimmy wouldn't sleep with the light off. Footsteps echoed somewhere from the very top of the house, and a man's insane laughter seemed to fill the upstairs empty rooms, and sounded as though someone was pacing from one side of the house to the other. The couple were beside themselves with fear and, although they loved the old house, they knew they could not carry on living there as long as the ghostly lodger remained.

Vera decided to ask one of the neighbours if they knew anything about the ghostly goings on at their home. Mrs Duggdale seemed quite surprised that anyone had moved into the empty house. 'It's old Tom Slattery,' she said in almost a whisper, folding her arms in front of her. 'He was mad, and lived in the attic.'

'But what happened to him?' Vera expected to hear a macabre story.

'His wife left him. She ran off with another man. Tom was heartbroken and lived and slept in the attic, where he eventually hanged himself. The people who lived there before you even brought a priest to exorcise the place, but even he left as fast as he came. The family moved out shortly after. The house was bombed of course, and it's been empty ever since. Old Tom won't move for anyone.'

The last straw came for Vera when she was cleaning the stairs one afternoon. It was a bright sunny day, and the sunlight was shining through the fanlight. She stopped what she was doing to watch the shadowy patterns that had been created by the sunlight shining through the grime on the glass. She thought she heard someone speaking in a low voice from the top of the stairs, and swung her head quickly round. She got the shock of her life when she saw an elderly man standing at the top, looking down at her and grinning. She froze to the spot and watched as the old man turned and then disappeared round the corner, laughing loudly.

The rice family moved out of the old house the following weekend, and the next family to live there did so for no longer than a week.

Billy says: Although the bricks and mortar of which the old house was constructed is no longer there, I am quite sure that Old Tom still resides in the attic, perhaps waiting for his wife's return.

You may think that you are alone, but you can never be sure who is watching – can you?

THINGS YOU WANTED TO KNOW

APPORTS: An apport is a small (or sometimes large) artefact, which appears seemingly from nowhere. This is a phenomenon that used to be commonplace in Victorian séances, and today is the hallmark of modern day Indian guru Satya Sai Baba.

ORBS: Popularised by the TV programme, Most Haunted, an orb is a concentration of spiritual energy, also known as a 'Spirit Light'. However, more often than not, orbs are caused by the geological phenomenon of 'Triboluminescence'; this is friction of crystal deposits below the ground of the location where the phenomena occurs.

HYPNOGOGIC STATE: As the mind is drifting into sleep, and is neither awake, nor asleep, is termed the hypnogogic state. Many of our so-called 'psychic' experiences occur during this state.

HYPNOPOMPIC STATE: The state of consciousness between waking and sleeping is the hypnopompic state.

HYPNOPAEDIA: Sleep learning; usually by playing a recorded message whilst you are sleeping.

AURA: Vaporous mass of electro-magnetic particles surrounding all living things. Multicoloured mist seen around the body.

TELEKINESIS: The movement of objects without physical means. Moving objects with the power of the mind.

TRIBOLUMINESCENCE: The geological phenomenon produced by friction of crystals below ground.

BIOLUMINESCENCE: The conversion of chemical energy to light energy, producing a glow around the body, and the phenomenon of the aura.

SÉANCE: Small circle of people devoted to communication with the so-called 'dead'. A séance also consists of people endeavouring to produce paranormal phenomena.

SÉANCE TRUMPET: Aluminium cone through which disembodied voices are heard.

PLANCHETTE: A small moveable device that holds a pencil, enabling it to write messages allegedly from a deceased person.

OUIJA BOARD: A board containing all the letters of the alphabet, and a small wooden pointer, spelling out words, allegedly coming from the spirit world.
MATERIALIZATION CABINET: A cabinet in which the medium is usually tied to a chair, primarily to avoid trickery. This form of mediumship is usually called 'Physical' or 'Materialization' mediumship, during which there is a production of ectoplasm.

MISCELLANEOUS PIECES

ACCUSED BY THE CHURCH

Christian fundamentalists have always decried mediums and psychics, protesting that their work is 'contrary to biblical teaching'. Although today religious attitudes are a little more relaxed, there is still a minority of so-called 'born again' Christians who decry mediums and clairvoyants, saying that they work with the devil. I am a Christian and my faith is important to me. It just so happens that I am also a medium, and I really do find the remarks made by born again Christians quite offensive. Some years ago my psychic shows would even be picketed by Christians, who would stand outside the venue handing out leaflets, warning those who were entering the theatre that they were 'dabbling' in the devil's work. Even though things have dramatically changed, there is still an underlying atmosphere of unrest, and the majority of those who have been brought up in Catholicism, still have an inherent dread of mediums.

In 1951 the government introduced the 'Fraudulent Mediums Act,' to prevent the unscrupulous 'charlatan' from exploiting the vulnerable and the gullible. In 1952, veteran Manchester medium, Norman England (now deceased) was brought to trial by the Catholic Church, accused of 'Foretelling the Future,' under the 1951 legislation. Although he pleaded 'not guilty' to the ridiculous charge, he was found guilty and ordered to pay a fine of £110, a lot of money in those days. The medium apparently used

Psychometry during a Spiritualist meeting, a method of divination, considered 'unacceptable' and illegal. In fact, technically speaking, Psychometry is still considered 'unacceptable' even today in Spiritualist meetings. To get round the legal obstacle, Spiritualist Churches have substituted Psychometry for 'Flower Sentience', as an accurate method of divination. Although in principle the process of flower sentience is the same as Psychometry, with this the person holds a flower for a short while before a service. The medium allegedly then gleans a broad spectrum of information about the holder of the flower. This, the law says, is quite acceptable.

HAVE YOU EVER SEEN....?

Did you know that you can't trust your eyes where ghostly phenomena are concerned. Ghostly manifestations can appear so fleetingly, that you are frequently left wondering if you saw anything at all. Did you know also, that people who lack imagination, very rarely 'see' ghosts?

Have you ever thought you have seen someone out of the corner of your eye, but when you turned your head to see what it was, there was nothing whatsoever there? The 'corner of the eye' phenomenon is one of the most common ways of seeing a so-called ghost. In fact, the majority of paranormal phenomena take place out of the corner of the eye. People usually see dancing figures of light, light anomalies, and even shadowy forms in this way. You didn't know that, did you?

INTERESTING FACTS

I have mentioned elsewhere that before man evolved even the most rudimentary form of speech, it is believed that our primitive forebears communicated their thoughts and feelings telepathically. In fact, the skill of mentally communicating, without the intermediary of the senses, has been lost, perhaps because there is no longer a need to do so. The association we once had with the supersensual side of the universe has long since been terminated and, as a direct consequence, we now view death as the Dark Intruder. Our primitive ancestors no doubt saw death as an extension of this life, and the actual transition from this world to the next as a journey almost across a bridge to a beautiful and yet uncharted land. It is a fallacy that anything can ever be killed or annihilated. There is no such actual state as death. There is only change, transmutation, growth, becoming a movement of matter, or of consciousness, from one condition to another. Nothing can ever die. However, in saying this, nothing in this world of form is permanent.

Contrary to popular belief, the Spirit World is not a place. It has nothing whatsoever to do with places. It is neither up, nor down, neither north, south, east nor west. The Spirit World orbits within and around the physical atom, and interpenetrates the physical world. It has no particular geographical position in the universe, and yet appears to be everywhere. In fact, the inhabitants of the Spirit World walk through and around us all the time, and are just as unaware of our presence, as we are unaware of theirs. We live, to all intents and purposes, in a multidimensional universe, in which there are worlds within worlds, each rising in a gradually ascending vibratory scale, from the very lowest planes of the physical world, to the extreme highest realms of the Spirit World. As the result of a temporary abnormality in the brain's electrical circuitry, we are sometimes fortunate enough to glimpse the inhabitants of these worlds and the environment in which they live. A medium is someone who lives his or her life permanently in this mental state and is therefore able to have supernatural experiences at any time. Although a medium is more in control of these experiences than the ordinary person, mediumistic abilities are not reliable, and results can neither be controlled, nor successfully predicted. No medium has the power to dictate exactly what is going to happen at any particular time and a so-called 'psychic demonstration' must always be perceived as an experiment.

That aspect of the Spiritual Universe often referred to as the 'Astral Plane', is also the abode of discarnate vagabonds, beings whose sole intention is to cause havoc and mischief in the physical world. These are the mischievous souls who lack spiritual direction and simply refuse to move on from the lower spheres into the wider and more spiritual dimensions of the so-called 'Heaven Worlds'. These astral vagabonds are those lacking spiritual understanding, and whose lives were controlled by their lower natures, perhaps through drug addiction, alcoholism, debauchery, and other lower passions. They constantly seek gratification through the kindred minds of those still living in a physical body. Evil beings do not suddenly become angelic once they pass over into the Spirit World. Evil persists on the other side of life, and very often contributes to the overwhelming feelings we sometimes experience in a so-called haunted house with an evil presence. Remember, though, the mind is the common denominator and very often creates its own demons. It is very often the fear that these evil astral vagabonds instil in us that holds the greatest danger. Nineteenth century dramatist and philosopher, Maurice Maeterlink, once said: 'The wise man is not he who sees, but he who seeing furthest, has the greatest love and understanding of all mankind. He who sees without loving and understanding, is only straining his eyes in the darkness'.

In the world of the Supernatural there is perhaps nothing whatsoever to fear, except fear itself.

THE FINAL WORD OF WARNING

My mother always said, 'A little knowledge is a dangerous thing,' at least where the paranormal is concerned. In fact, great caution must always be exercised when one is dealing with things of this nature. Although over the past 10-years-or-so great scientific strides have been made in the exploration of the world of metaphysical subjects, I do believe that we are no nearer now to understanding the true nature of discarnate beings and the worlds which they inhabit. Over the last few years or so, I have concluded that very little takes place outside of the human mind, and that the mind is the common denominator where the paranormal is concerned.

For example, if I were to take a friend into an old house, which I knew to be haunted, but chose not to divulge this information to him, the chances are that he would neither see nor sense anything out of the ordinary. On the other hand, if I allowed him to be privy to the knowledge that the house was, in fact, haunted, the spooky scenario would have already been created long before he walked through the door, and he would then probably be far more receptive to any paranormal activity.

Very few people would actually be afraid to spend the night in a haunted house, as long as a few friends accompanied them. But it is a completely different story when we are faced with the prospect of spending the night in such a place alone. The mind creates its own ghosts and demons and is very often able to perceive what is not really there. The truth is that it is in our psychological make-up to embroider our experiences and create scenarios that appear more frightening than they really are. I am quite certain that this is the reason why there is a universal fascination for ghost stories. The process of reading a spooky tale allows the reader to keep a safe distance and to experience the weird happenings at second hand, knowing that at any moment the reality of what is being read can be terminated, simply by closing the book. I suppose this is the great difference between a medium and an ordinary person. A medium possesses the ability to control what he or she experiences and the ordinary person does not.

Fear only arises from an experience of something that we do not fully understand. The phenomenon of a ghost is very often beyond the normal person's comprehension, especially when somebody else has passed on the ghostly tale to them. However, it is a completely different story when one experiences the ghostly phenomenon at first hand.

Ghosts, too, are very often not all that they seem. One of the biggest misconceptions about ghost and apparitions is that they are always the spirits of the so-called 'dead'. This is most certainly not the case, as I have explained at the beginning of this book. The majority of paranormal appearances are merely supersensitive images, captured in the psychic atmosphere. They do not possess intelligence, or even a rudimentary form of consciousness, but are just like photographic images in the surrounding air.

Everything that possesses the substance of emotion and thought power is capable of energising its surrounding environment and impregnating it with such intensity as to leave an everlasting impression. These impressions are replayed rather like watching the DVD of an old movie and are nearly always precipitated by an incarnate mind. As I have explained many times before, there are, of course, the exceptions. Some ghosts are the apparitions of the actual spirit of the so-called 'dead' person who simply refuses to move on. Very often it is a love of habit that exerts the strongest and most powerful control over the discarnate spirit's life. This is why the old man is often seen sitting in his favourite pub, in the same corner where he always used to sit when he was alive. Or why the lady in white is often seen casually strolling through the garden, following the same route she always took in life. There is an extremely thin veil separating this world from the next and, occasionally, that veil is briefly lifted, allowing us mortals the privilege of glimpsing those things that have been and sometimes those things that are yet to be.

Always remember: somebody, somewhere, is watching you!

Media Reviews

What the media said of Spooky Liverpool

• A spine-tingling collection of stories that will appeal to anyone fascinated by ghosts, and the spirit word. A book well worth making contact with.

- Liverpool ECHO

• A very enjoyable read. It is hard to put down once you have picked it up as Billy is your guide on a journey into the unknown.

- Liverpool Daily Post

• It's the type of book you should always have on your holidays. You can dip in and dip out or like me read it all in one go.

- Actress Eithne Brown - A very good read

With Thanks

From the Author

I would, first of all, like to dedicate this book to my wife, Dolly, who helped me immensely in preparing the copy for Spooky Liverpool 2.

Also, I would like a mention for our cat, Pessy, who, sadly passed away whilst writing this book.

A special thanks to Peter Grant for his support over the years; Ken Rogers for taking a chance and showing an interest in my books.

And a big thank you to Emma Smart for all her hard work, and for putting up with all my phone calls.

Design thanks to Colin Sumpter and to Jason Roberts for the atmospheric spooky cover.

Thanks too, to the rest of the staff at Trinity Mirror for all their hard work.

I would also like to thank Mike Chapple from the Daily Post for showing an interest in what I do.

And finally, you dear reader.

Billy Roberts
2008
www.billyroberts.co.uk

ABOUT THE AUTHOR

Billy Roberts has been a psychic since he was a child and has been a professional stage medium at home and abroad for more than 25 years.

He travels all over the world with his psychic stage shows, seminars and workshops.

Billy is regarded as one of the UK's leading authorities on the paranormal.

He appears regularly on TV, radio and in the national and regional press.

Billy is also seen at many book signings enjoying the chance to meet his fans that have supported him and his wide range of books.

Billy has also written a children's book The Magic Locker published by Trinity Mirror which helps Alder Hey's Imagine Appeal where he spent a part of his childhood.

Like Spooky Liverpool, his first book in this series, he has been personally involved in the tales and extensively researched others - many of which were passed on to him by fans and ghost story lovers for which he remains very grateful.

If you have a ghost story to tell, contact www.billyroberts.co.uk